FRACTURE IN POLYMERS

Fracture in Polymers

E. H. ANDREWS

AMERICAN ELSEVIER
NEW YORK

AMERICAN ELSEVIER PUBLISHING COMPANY, INC.
52 Vanderbilt Avenue New York, New York 10017
First published 1968
Library of Congress Catalog Card Number: 67–19742
© 1968 E. H. Andrews
Published in Great Britain by
Oliver and Boyd Limited

Printed in Great Britain by
Aberdeen University Press

Foreword by Sir Harry Melville, K.C.B., F.R.S.

There is an abundance of scientific and technical literature concerning the synthesis, structure and characterisation   polymers. This is to be expected since there are limitless possibilities in the field and as a result of the work described many unique polymers have been evolved. Polymers are materials to be used, equally, for an endless variety of purposes. Although an extensive empirical knowledge has been built up concerning the use of these substances, the physics of their properties has not been dealt with extensively. Apart from the problem of correlating chemical structure with mechanical behaviour there is much to be done in understanding such vitally important phenomena as structural failure or fracture. Unlike crystalline materials, polymers have a much more complicated morphology and, what is more, the morphology can change while the specimen is subjected to forces that lead to crack formation, propagation of cracks and ultimately complete failure. Dr. Andrews has set himself the task to assemble existing knowledge both theoretical and practical. He has collated a wide variety of data and has produced as a result a most readable and logical approach to this subject. Much of the material discussed is still rather qualitative and much of the fundamental knowledge about polymers that have been fairly extensively investigated from the mechanical viewpoint is also lacking. There is another merit of the book. It shows up clearly where further work must be done. It will therefore stimulate the readers in their respective fields of interest to set about producing the data and ideas that will provide the very necessary advances in this subject so that polymeric materials can be used to do a specific job in the most precise and efficient ways that can be devised. For those who are planning instruction in these fields the book will be a most welcome addition to the libraries for it will save an immense time in assembling material in a coherent fashion for instructional purposes.

Author's Preface

This book had its beginnings in a series of invited lectures given at the College of Aeronautics, Cranfield, and it is a measure of the rapid growth and increasing significance of the subject that it has found a place in at least one academic syllabus. As Sir Harry Melville points out in his Foreword, the physics of polymers is a neglected field and this is undoubtedly due to the lag of science behind technology which so often occurs when discoveries or inventions (in this case those of the polymer chemist) are promptly and successfully exploited. The technological 'explosion' in the field of polymers has been truly impressive and some of today's commonest plastics were unknown ten years ago. The physicist, however, need not feel left behind by these developments. It is only now, as engineers are becoming increasingly interested in structural applications for plastics that the gaps in our physical understanding of these materials are being exposed. It is not enough to rely on past experience with other solids such as metals; polymers exhibit a whole host of unfamiliar, and often unexpected, properties.

Fracture is, of course, a phenomenon of great scientific interest as well as practical importance, and it is hoped that this book may be of interest and service to the purist as well as the engineering scientist. It may have some appeal even to the metallurgist since a familiarity with materials as such is often expected of him today.

My purpose in writing has been to present a comprehensive, logical and readable account of the subject. These aims are, to a certain extent, conflicting and a balance has had to be struck between exhaustiveness and clarity. If either has been sacrificed, it is the first of these and as a result some excellent research work has received less attention than it deserves.

My gratitude is due to many colleagues and fellow workers in the field, in U.S.A. and U.S.S.R. as well as in England, for their interest and for their willingness to share with me the results of their studies and their current ideas. I am indebted also to those, particularly Dr. A. J. Kennedy and Prof. D. W. Saunders, who encourged me to write the book, and to my colleagues at Queen Mary College for helpful criticism during its preparation.

E. H. ANDREWS
Queen Mary College,
London, E.1

Acknowledgements

The author is indebted to the following sources for permission to reproduce figures and diagrams, as well as to the authors of the publications (to which references are given in the relevant captions) from which they are drawn.

Ind. Eng. Chem.	Figs. 2.15, 3.4
J. appl. Phys.	Figs. 1.12, 1.13, 3.9, 5.20, 5.21, 6.10, 6.12
J. appl. Polym. Sci.	Figs. 3.1, 5.3, 5.17, 5.18, 5.19, 5.27, 6.21
J. bas. Engng	Fig. 5.13
J. Colloid Sci.	Fig. 1.22
J. Polym. Sci.	Figs. 1.10, 1.21, 2.17, 2.18, 4.4, 4.7, 5.5, 5.7, 5.8
Kolloid Zeit.	Fig. 1.20
Kunstoffe	Fig. 3.11
Natural Rubber Producers Research Assn	Figs. 2.16, 3.13, 3.14, 5.22, 5.23
Plastics (*London*)	Figs. 2.2, 2.3, 2.4, 2.5, 2.10, 2.13, 2.22, 2.23, 2.24
Polymer	Figs. 2.7, 2.8, 2.14
Proc. Phys. Soc.	Fig. 6.3
Proc. Roy. Soc.	Figs. 2.19, 3.10, 3.17, 3.19, 5.11, 5.12
S.C.I.	Fig. 2.6
Soviet Phys.	Figs. 3.5, 6.17
Trans. Faraday Soc.	Fig. 3.2
Trans. I.R.I.	Fig. 5.6
Wear	Fig. 3.12

Contents

Chapter 6
FRACTURE SURFACES

CHAPTER 1

The Nature of
Polymeric Solids

1.1 LONG CHAIN MOLECULES

Polymers are materials composed of long, chain-like molecules in which the atoms are bound together by strong co-valent bonds. In some cases the molecules themselves are connected by similar bonds to form a three-dimensional network which, in one sense, constitutes a single gigantic molecule. Chain-like molecules are formed during the process of 'polymerisation' in which small molecules link together either di-functionally or tri-functionally to form chains or networks respectively. A simple case of the former process is the polymerisation of ethylene gas at high temperature and pressure to form polyethylene. The breakdown of the double bond in ethylene provides each of the constituent carbon atoms with a 'free' valency which is satisfied by combination with other such units to produce a chain containing perhaps ten thousand carbon atoms (Fig. 1.1). The

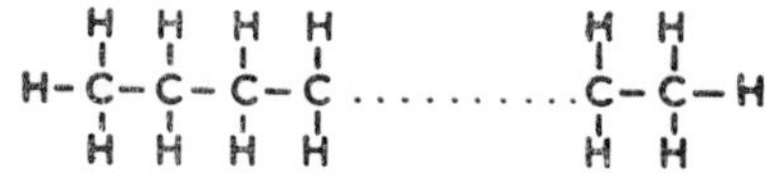

$$
\begin{array}{ccccccc}
& H & H & H & H & & H & H \\
& | & | & | & | & & | & | \\
H- & C- & C- & C- & C & \cdots\cdots\cdots & C- & C-H \\
& | & | & | & | & & | & | \\
& H & H & H & H & & H & H
\end{array}
$$

FIG. 1.1   Polyethylene molecule.

carbon-atom 'backbone' is a feature of most organic polymers, though other atoms or groups of atoms do often occur in conjunction with carbon in the molecular backbone.

An example of network formation arising from tri-functional groups is shown in Fig. 1.2 where the formation of a phenol-formaldehyde resin is represented. In this case there are two reacting species, phenol (C_6H_5OH) and formaldehyde (CH_2O), and the latter is

1

capable of uniting two molecules of the former eliminating water and leaving four unreacted hydrogens on each of the phenol molecules. Because space around the phenol molecule is limited only two of these sites can provide further linkages, but this is sufficient to provide for a three-dimensional polymer network to be built up. If there is only

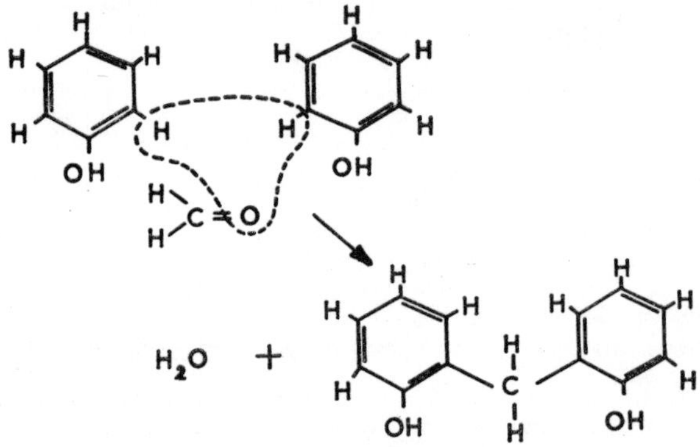

FIG. 1.2   Formation of phenol formaldehyde.

a small degree of tri-functional behaviour in a polymerisation process, branching of the otherwise linear molecules can occur without the formation of a network, and this is a feature of low density poly-ethylene (Fig. 1.3).

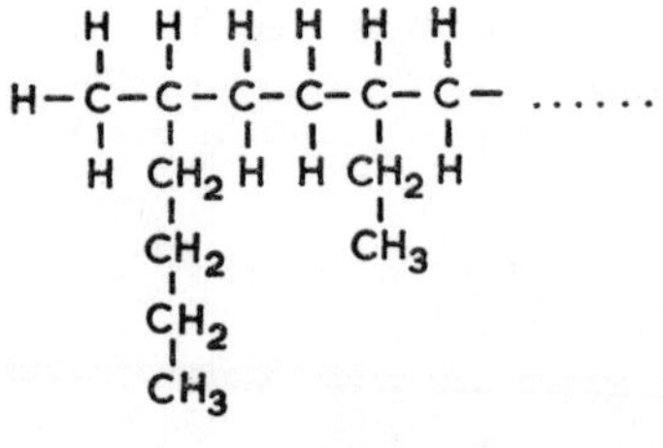

FIG. 1.3   Branching in polyethylene.

Carbon lends itself to the formation of polymeric compounds because of its fourfold chemical valency and its readiness to combine with itself and with small atoms such as hydrogen, nitrogen and oxygen to form stable macromolecular substances. This propensity is shared to a large extent by silicon and to a lesser extent by other group IV elements. In the case of silicon a very large number of polymeric compounds are known, namely the silicate minerals. Silicon compounds, however, differ from organic polymers in several important respects and in the solid state there is little physical resemblance between the two kinds of polymer. Silicon polymers, being based on the —SiO_4— unit, exhibit much stronger inter-chain

TABLE 1.1

Polypropylene	H H | | —C—C— | | H CH_3	tough, crystalline
Polyvinylchloride (PVC)	H H | | —C—C— | | H Cl	glassy (leathery when plasticised)
Polystyrene	H H | | —C—C— | | H C_6H_5	glassy
Polybutadiene	H H | | —C—C— | | H $CH:CH_2$	rubberlike
Polymethylmethacrylate (PMMA)	H CH_3 | | —C—C— | | H $CO \cdot O \cdot CH_3$	glassy
Polytetrafluorethylene (PTFE)	F F | | —C—C— | | F F	tough, crystalline

Polycarbonate of
bisphenol A
	CH_3
	    |
	—O—⬡—C—⬡—O·CO—
	    |
	CH_3
		glassy

forces than carbon-based polymers and are generally completely crystalline. Rotation of the chain about its 'backbone' Si—O bonds is thus far less easy than for the C—C bond, so that even non-crystalline silicon polymers such as fused silica are brittle, glassy materials up to a very high temperature. In organic polymers, on the other hand, low inter-chain forces and chain flexibility give rise to low softening and melting points, imperfect crystallinity and low mechanical rigidity, characteristics usually associated with the materials commonly called 'polymers'. The term polymer is used in this sense in all that follows, most of the materials considered being compounds of carbon. There is one commercially important exception to what has been said about silicon-based polymers, namely the silicone rubbers which have a Si—O—Si backbone and which possess mechanical properties very similar to those of carbon-based rubbers. Some common organic polymers are given in Table 1.1 which shows the repeat-unit or *mer* from which the molecular chain is built up.

1.2 CROSS-LINKS AND NETWORKS

It was pointed out earlier that some polymers occur in the form of long chains whilst others from the outset consist of a random three-dimensional network. The former are known as thermoplastics because an increase in temperature provides the molecules with sufficient vibrational energy to overcome the weak inter-chain forces (consisting of Van der Waals' and hydrogen bonds) and thus to undergo relative motion or flow. The material enters a 'plastic' condition in which it can be moulded, extruded and so on, but regains a rigid consistency when the temperature is allowed to fall. In a network of molecules such relative movement cannot occur without the breakage of co-valent bonds so that these materials must be polymerised into the desired shape during the manufacture of an article and cannot thereafter be re-moulded. Because of this, highly cross-linked network materials are called 'thermosetting resins'.

There exists a third possibility that a thermoplastic may be transformed into a thermosetting material by the introduction of random inter-molecular cross-links (Fig. 1.4) and this is what happens in the case of most rubbers. A thermally-activated cross-linking agent (for example, sulphur) is mixed into the original thermoplastic material which is then moulded thermoplastically before the cross-linking reaction takes place. According to the amount of cross-linking introduced a wide variety of properties may be obtained. Materials may be made in which a relatively small number of cross-links impart immunity to creep to an otherwise highly deformable solid or, alternatively, materials of a glassy consistency in which a large cross-linking density has effectively immobilised molecular movement. Cross-links may be introduced into most thermo-plastics, including polyethylene and polymethylmethacrylate (abbreviated PMMA), as well as into rubbers; the cross-links may involve

FIG. 1.4   Cross-linking of a thermoplastic.

'bridges' of atoms foreign to the polymer, as in the cross-linking of rubber by polysulphide linkages, or may be produced by directly linking two backbone atoms in neighbouring molecules. Cross-links may be introduced by chemical reaction or by high-energy radiation.

1.3 MOLECULAR FLEXIBILITY

All long-chain molecules are potentially flexible because of the possibility of rotation about C—C or C—O backbone single bonds. Consider first of all the simple molecule of ethane.

$$\begin{array}{cc} H & H \\ | & | \\ H-C-C-H \\ | & | \\ H & H \end{array}$$

In three dimensions this molecule has the form sketched in Fig. 1.5 and there is evidently no reason why one methyl (CH_3) group should not rotate relative to the other about the C—C bond as axis. There does exist one source of hindrance to such rotation, however, in that certain rotational positions bring the hydrogen atoms of one methyl group closer to those of the other group than do alternative positions as can be seen by considering Fig. 1.6. In a full 360° rotation three identical 'energy barriers' have to be overcome and this is pictured in Fig. 1.7 which shows the internal energy of the molecule plotted against the relative rotational angle of the two methyl groups. If one of the hydrogens in each methyl group were replaced by a different

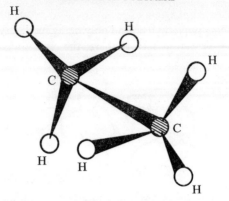

FIG. 1.5   Three dimensional sketch of the ethane molecule.

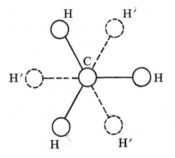

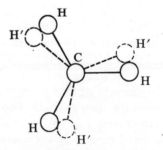

FIG. 1.6   End-on view of ethane
molecule showing (*top*) low energy
and (*bottom*) high energy rotational
configurations.

atom, chlorine for example, then the three energy maxima would no longer be equal in height.

Let us now transfer these ideas to the case of a long chain polymer Here in three dimensions we have a zig-zag arrangement of atoms in

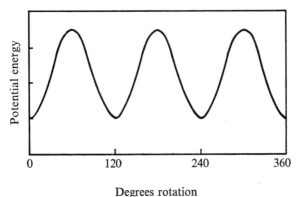

Degrees rotation

FIG. 1.7   Energy barriers to rotation about the C—C bond.

the backbone since one C—C bond is always at an angle of 109° to the next. This means that rotation about a single bond in the molecule can cause wholesale movement of one portion of the

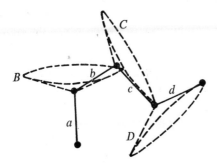

FIG. 1.8   Possible configurations of the C—C 'backbone' in a polymer molecule.

molecule relative to the remainder and rotation about *all* bonds will allow the molecule to assume a randomly coiled configuration. This can be seen from Fig. 1.8 where some possible configurations of a very short succession of C—C linkages are shown. If the first bond *a* is held stationary the second bond b can lie anywhere on the surface of a cone B with its apex at the second carbon atom bringing the third carbon atom to any point on the rim of the cone B. The same process is repeated for the third bond and so on; obviously the number of possible chain configurations is infinite and because of thermal motion the configuration of any given molecule is constantly changing. It can be shown, however, that there exists a statistically most probable distance between the *ends* of a chain of freely jointed links provided the orientation of each link with respect to its neighbours is random, and this distance is found to be proportional to the square root of the number of links.[1]

A random coil configuration will be that favoured by the molecule since it is the most probable form. Any other form will involve a restriction on the choice of orientations between successive linkages; the number N of possible ways of achieving the form will also be limited and the 'configurational entropy' (defined as $S_c = S_0 + k \log N$ where S_0 and k are constants) will be smaller. In the extreme case of a planar zig-zag arrangement in which the chain molecule is extended to its maximum end-to-end length, N will be unity and the entropy will be a minimum. To extend the molecule from a random coil to an elongated form thus involves a decrease in entropy which by the second law of thermodynamics requires work to be done on the system (internal energy being assumed constant). On the other hand the reverse process of collapse to the randomly coiled form will release energy and minimise the free energy of the system, so that the random arrangement is seen to be the most favoured, the form to which the molecule will always naturally return.

Several points emerge from this brief consideration of molecular flexibility. Firstly, as we have seen, the molecules of a polymer will in their undisturbed condition be randomly coiled with a most probable end-to-end distance proportional to the square root of the number of links. By doing work on the system we can extend a molecule to its maximum length which is proportional to the number of links, i.e., we can achieve a strain of the order of $n^{\frac{1}{2}}$ where n is the number of freely jointed linkages. This number n is not equal to the number of mers in the molecule because there is not perfect freedom at the 'joints', but it nevertheless turns out [2] that only a few mers are required to constitute an 'equivalent' freely jointed link and n is still a large number, If, for example, ten mers are equivalent to a free link, and there are, say, 4000 mers in a particular molecule, the value of n is

400 and the possible strain is of the order of 20. Detailed considerations reduce this estimate to about 10 but it is nevertheless evident that very large recoverable strains can occur in polymeric solids as a result of molecular uncoiling. Recoverable strains approaching ten are, in fact, readily observed in rubber and the phenomenon of chain uncoiling is thus often referred to as rubberlike elasticity. It is in distinct contrast to the phenomenon of elasticity in rigid materials which arises from the distortion of atomic bonds and in which the internal energy of the system is increased by the work done on it, the change in entropy being relatively negligible.[1] In this form of elasticity strains cannot exceed about 0·2 since higher deformation must result in the rupture of atomic bonds, and even this figure is never achieved in real solids because of inherent weaknesses which lead to yield or fracture at much lower strains. Another important feature of rubberlike elasticity is the low stress necessary to produce a given strain, Young's moduli in elastomers being typically some 10^3 to 10^4 times smaller than in materials such as metals and ceramics.

Although reversible chain uncoiling is most obviously evidenced in rubbers, large reversible deformations are also found in other polymers. Low density polyethylene, for example, may be extended several hundred percent at room temperature, though the deformation appears to be permanent (i.e., plastic) and no recovery is observed. If the specimen is heated to about 130°C however, almost complete recovery occurs proving that the deformation must have arisen from the uncoiling of molecules without wholesale slipping.

1.4 THE GLASS TRANSITION

(i) *Hindrances to flexibility*

So far we have discussed the deformation characteristics of a single polymer chain and have seen how large *recoverable* deformations are to be expected as a result of chain uncoiling. This is, of course, in addition to any large, *irrecoverable* deformations such as those involved when thermoplastics are moulded and which are caused by the slipping or flow of the molecule relative to its surroundings. We must now consider carefully the effect of the surrounding molecules upon the deformation of any one of them. It is obvious that the presence of neighbouring molecules in a polymeric solid will greatly hinder the process of rotation about backbone atomic bonds since such rotation inevitably gives rise to translation of parts of the molecule involved. Such 'wriggling' movements as are necessary to accommodate rotations can only occur as the surrounding molecules

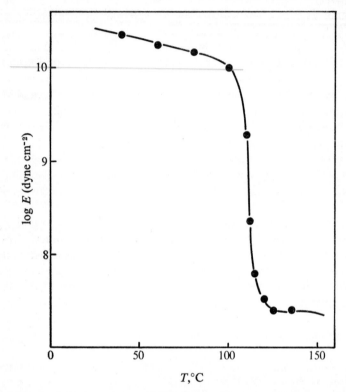

FIG. 1.9 Young's modulus of PMMA as a function of temperature (after Tobolsky[3]).

give way, and could not take place at all unless they did so. These inter-molecular or steric hindrances to rotation are far greater than the intra-molecular barriers discussed earlier in connection with the ethane molecule and are of such a magnitude that many polymeric solids at room temperature are relatively hard and unyielding. As the temperature is raised, however, a point is reached where even these materials become rubbery, i.e., their Young's modulus falls rapidly with rising temperature to a value typical of a rubber and rubberlike elasticity is observed. This is illustrated in Fig. 1.9 for PMMA.[3] In uncross-linked polymers molecular flow will also occur at elevated temperatures, though even in this liquid condition a large degree of rubberlike behaviour is found, since chain entanglements may provide effective temporary cross-linkage.

This transition from a glassy to a rubberlike consistency is characteristic of polymeric solids and is referred to as the glass-rubber or simply the glass transition. It occurs when the thermal energy of the molecules becomes sufficiently great to overcome the barriers to rotation and molecular movement. At all temperatures the molecules are in a kind of Brownian motion, a motion that tends to overcome these barriers, but below a certain temperature movement is oscillatory rather than rotational and cannot lead to rubberlike deformation of the molecules under small applied forces. However, the likelihood P of the barriers to rotation being surmounted increases rapidly with temperature according to an Arrhenius-type relation,

$$P = \exp\left(-F/kT\right) \tag{1.1}$$

where k is Boltzmann's constant and F is the free energy of activation of the process. As the temperature rises the frequency of rotations increases until it reaches significant proportions on the time-scale of the experiment. At this point the likelihood of accommodative movement in the environment of a given molecule is sufficiently high to facilitate rotation, and rubber like behaviour is observed.

The 'time-scale of the experiment' is important since the temperature at which the transition occurs is found to depend upon the speed (or frequency, if an alternating stress is applied) at which the modulus is measured. This can be expressed explicitly in terms of equation (1.1) by saying that the quantity tP where t is the time of the experiment, must achieve a certain value for the onset of the transition to be recorded.

$$\log tP = \text{constant} = -F/kT + \log t$$

And differentiating,

$$\Delta(\log t) = -\frac{F}{kT^2}\Delta T. \tag{1.2}$$

An increase in log time is thus equivalent to a decrease in temperature, so that an apparent shift in the transition temperature is to be expected for each decade change in the time scale of the experiment.

We shall see presently that this statement is an over simplification and only harmonises with experiment if F is allowed to vary with temperature.

(ii) *Free volume*

For various reasons it is difficult to define the glass transition accurately in terms of mechanical properties such as elastic modulus, and a more fundamental definition is available in terms of the volume changes within the material.

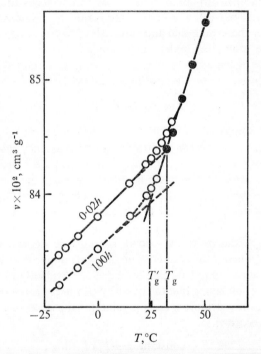

FIG. 1.10 Specific volume of an amorphous polymer as a function of temperature for two rates of cooling (after Kovacs[4]).

A graph of specific volume against temperature for an amorphous polymer is shown by the solid line in Fig. 1.10 and consists of two linear portions joined by a short transition range.[4] The extrapolated linear regions meet at a point which is dependent upon the rate of heating or cooling, falling at a lower temperature for slow measurements than for rapid ones. This is indicated by the dotted line in Fig. 1.10 which refers to a rate nearly 10^4 times slower than the solid line. Although, however, the 'transition temperature' is again rate dependent it is found to approach a limiting value for measurements made over a realisable time scale. The glass transition temperature,

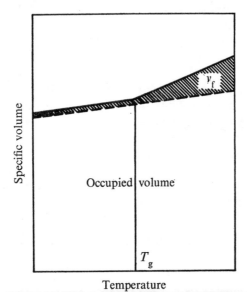

FIG. 1.11 The contribution of free volume (v_f) to the expansion of an amorphous polymer (after Ferry[5]).

T_g, of a polymer can thus be defined as the temperature of intersection of the two linear portions of the specific volume-temperature curve, the experiment being carried out over a specified time scale.

The break in the curve of Fig. 1.10 can be explained in terms of 'free volume', i.e., the excess volume occupied by unit mass of the material over and above that necessary to accommodate the atoms in the closest packing permitted by the bond structure. Even at the lowest temperatures some free volume will exist because the material is amorphous, i.e., has not attained crystalline order, but this free volume will be constant up to a certain temperature whilst all thermal expansion results from increased thermal motion of the atoms, i.e., from solid state expansion. As T_g is approached, however, and intramolecular rotations begin to occur at a significant rate, the possibility arises of temporary 'holes' being created in the material as a result of such movements. Upon the solid-state expansion, therefore, is now superimposed an *expansion of free volume* which has the effect of increasing the total rate of expansion to that more typical of a liquid. This is all shown diagrammatically in Fig. 1.11. The actual value of the free volume, expressed as a fraction f of the total volume is of the order of 0·025 at the glass transition temperature and does not differ greatly from one polymer to another.[5]

(iii) *The WLF equation*

Let us now return to our consideration of molecular mobility and suppose that the probability of rotational movement is governed, not by the Arrhenius equation of classical rate-theory as assumed previously, but by a relationship involving free volume. Clearly the greater the fractional free volume, f, the easier will such movement be. If f is zero the probability must reduce to zero whilst as f tends to infinity, the probability must approach unity. These requirements are satisfied by an equation of the form

$$P = \exp\left(-B/f\right) \tag{1.3}$$

where B is a constant. If, as before, we put $tP = \text{constant}$ for any particular set of properties to be observed (e.g., some arbitrary value of elastic modulus) we obtain

$$\log tP = -B/f + \log t = \text{constant}$$

$$\Delta \log t = B\Delta(1/f). \tag{1.4}$$

That is, a change in the time scale of the experiment is equivalent to a change in fractional free volume. But from the normal law of thermal expansion

$$f = f_0 + \alpha_f(T - T_0) \tag{1.5}$$

where the suffix zero denotes some arbitrary reference point on the absolute temperature scale, and α_f is the coefficient of expansion of free volume. Thus

$$\Delta \log t = B(1/f - 1/f_0) = \frac{-(B/f_0)\Delta T}{(f_0/\alpha_f) + \Delta T}. \tag{1.6}$$

This equation signifies that a shift in time scale will produce the same change in mechanical properties (at least, in those dependent upon the rotational movement of molecular segments) as will a related change in temperature given by equation (1.6). Equation (1.6) is sometimes known as the Williams-Landel-Ferry (WLF) equation since it was first obtained empirically by these workers.[6] It is a far more acceptable equation than the Arrhenius relation (1.2) and undoubtedly reflects far better the molecular mechanisms involved in the deformation of amorphous polymers. The reader is referred elsewhere[7] for a more rigid derivation of equation (1.6).

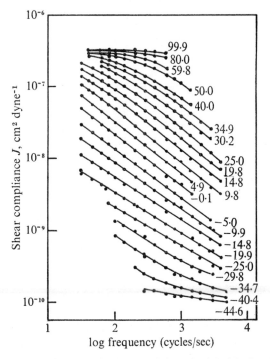

FIG. 1.12   Dynamic shear compliance of polyisobutylene as a function of frequency for 22 different temperatures (after Fitzgerald, Grandine and Ferry[8]).

An example of the application of the WLF equation is given in Figs. 1.12 and 1.13. In Fig. 1.12 the dynamic shear compliance (the inverse of the shear modulus) is plotted for polyisobutylene as a function of the frequency of application of the load in cycles per second.[8] Data for 22 different temperatures is shown. By employing the WLF equation to shift the curves along the log frequency axis by appropriate amounts, determined of course by the temperatures, a single master curve (Fig. 1.13) is obtained. The 'shift factor' $\Delta \log t$

is usually denoted by log a_T and the constants of equation (1.6) are empirically determined. These constants, B, f and α_f are found to differ very little from one polymer to another providing the reference temperature T_0 is chosen to be T_g, the value of which of course changes from polymer to polymer. This is reasonable since at T_g the physical situation in all amorphous polymers can be regarded as

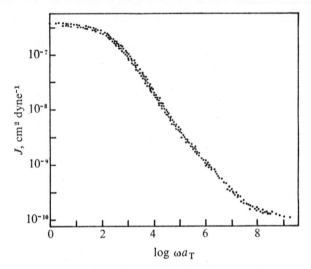

FIG. 1.13 The data of Fig. 1.12 reduced to a single master curve by use of the WLF relation; ω is the angular frequency (after Fitzgerald, Grandine and Ferry[8]).

similar. The greatest virtue of this method of treating data (the method of 'reduced variables') is that it enables a large quantity of information to be displayed in a particularly simple way and also emphasises the time-temperature dependence of mechanical properties which is usually expressed by the term 'visco-elasticity'. It should be emphasised that the WLF equation applies only to amorphous polymers and then only at temperatures above the glass transition, i.e., under conditions where the free volume is expanding.

1.5 MECHANICAL PROPERTIES OF POLYMERS

From what has already been said it will be clear that the long-chain molecules of polymers impart to such materials mechanical characteristics of a kind not encountered in metals and ceramics. Below we consider briefly some of these properties dealing in turn with the stress-strain curve, elastic modulus and mechanical hysteresis.

(i) *The stress-strain curve*

Any graphical representation of the dependence of stress upon strain in a body can be called a stress-strain curve. Usually a simple system of stress is employed, such as simple tension in the x direction of a system of cartesian co-ordinates, thus

$$\left. \begin{aligned} \sigma_x &= \sigma \\ \sigma_y &= \sigma_z = 0 \end{aligned} \right\} \quad \text{normal components of stress}$$

$$\tau_{xy} = \tau_{yz} = \tau_{zx} = 0 \quad \text{shear components of stress} \quad (1.7)$$

or simple shear in which, e.g., only τ_{xy} is non zero. In general, however, it should be remembered that there are six possible independent stress components and six corresponding strains (direct and shear) so that the total picture involves 36 coefficients (or elastic constants) relating stresses to strains, i.e., 36 'stress-strain' curves defining a general state of deformation under stress. Symmetry considerations reduce this number to 21 in anisotropic materials, but this is still a large number. If the material is isotropic there are only two independent elastic constants. In referring to the 'stress-strain' curve of a polymer we must therefore remember that it is just one particularly simple representation of the response of the material to stress. Unless otherwise stated the stress-strain curves referred to will be those relating a simple tensile-stress to the corresponding strain. The tensile stress, σ, is given by the force on unit area of *deformed* cross-section (not original cross-section) and the tensile strain ε by the increase in length of an element of the material divided by its original length. The 'extension ratio' λ in the material is the deformed length divided by the original length, so that $\lambda = \varepsilon + 1$.

In many materials, including polymers at very low strains, the stress and strain are linearly related (Hooke's law).

$$\left. \begin{aligned} \sigma &= E\varepsilon \\ \tau &= G\gamma \end{aligned} \right\} \quad (1.8)$$

where γ is the shear strain. The coefficients E and G are the Young's modulus and shear (or rigidity) modulus respectively. The bulk modulus, K, can similarly be defined as

$$K = -P/(\Delta V/V) \quad (1.9)$$

where P is the pressure and $(\Delta V/V)$ the bulk strain in a volume V of the material. These three moduli are related by a dimensionless variable, Poisson's ratio, which can be defined as

$$\mu = \tfrac{1}{2}[1 - V^{-1}(\partial V / \partial \varepsilon)] \qquad (1.10)$$

and is a measure of the lateral contraction accompanying a longitudinal extension. The following relations apply

$$\begin{aligned} E &= 2G(1+\mu) \\ E &= 3K(1-2\mu) \end{aligned} \qquad (1.11)$$

For an incompressible material (approximated by a soft rubber) $\mu = 0{\cdot}5$ but for most homogeneous, isotropic materials it has a value in the region of $0{\cdot}2$. As $\mu \to 0{\cdot}5$ it is clear from equation (1.11) that $E \to 3G$ and $K \to \infty$.

It is often convenient to use, not the elastic moduli defined above but their inverses, the so-called 'compliances'. These are denoted as follows.

$$\left.\begin{array}{lll} \text{Tensile compliance} & D = E^{-1} \\ \text{Shear compliance} & J = G^{-1} \\ \text{Bulk compliance} & B = K^{-1} \end{array}\right\} \qquad (1.12)$$

The stress-strain curves of actual polymers vary greatly and obedience to Hooke's law is limited to small strains. At such strains typical values for the moduli in solid polymeric systems are as follows:

$$\left.\begin{array}{l} E,\, G \sim 10^5 \text{ to } 10^{12} \text{ dyne cm}^{-2} \\ K \sim 10^{10} \text{ to } 10^{12} \text{ dyne cm}^{-2} \end{array}\right\}$$

$(K$ is always greater than $G)$

The moduli are functions both of time and temperature so that a wide range of values in, say, G may be encountered under different conditions in the same polymer.

As stress increases the slope of the stress-strain curve usually falls, i.e., prior to yield, the curve is concave to the strain axis. Fig. 1.14 (a) is typical of a glassy polymer like polymethylmethacrylate (PMMA) at 20°C. If the temperature is raised the stress-strain behaviour of PMMA follows the pattern shown in Fig. 1.14, with a declining Young's modulus and the eventual appearance of a yield point. Meanwhile the fracture stress σ_f decreases and the fracture strain ε_f rises, increasing rapidly once the yield phenomenon is established. The stress and strain at yield are denoted σ_f and ε_f respectively.

When a marked yield point, with a decrease in stress, occurs in the tensile stress-strain curve the specimen under test is often found to have some local reduction in cross-section area, a phenomenon referred to as 'necking'. In cases such as PMMA cited above the neck continues to reduce in cross-section area until fracture occurs, but in many semi-crystalline polymers the neck runs along the specimen which thus elongates, often at constant load. Once the

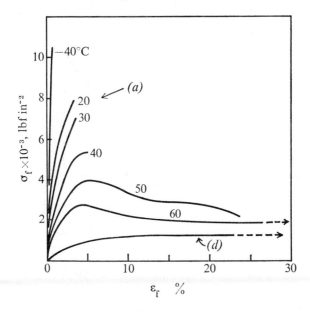

FIG. 1.14 Stress strain behaviour of PMMA at various temperatures. Curve d shows rubberlike behaviour of a cross-linked thermoplastic above T_g.

whole gauge length of the specimen has been reduced to a uniform cross-section by this process the force again begins to rise until fracture takes place. This is shown in Fig. 1.15. Such behaviour is often called 'cold drawing' though there may (or may not) be a local rise in temperature at the 'shoulder' of the neck where most of the deformation occurs over a small region. The process clearly involves some form of 'strain hardening' since the reduced cross-section could not otherwise bear the full load on the specimen.

If the temperature of test is increased sufficiently the polymer becomes either fluid or rubberlike depending on the absence or

3

presence of cross-links. If cross-links are present to prevent the molecules slipping past one another the characteristics of rubberlike elasticity are observed in the stress-strain curve (Fig. 1.14(d)). As discussed earlier, rubberlike elasticity arises from the elongation of randomly coiled molecules and the 'restoring force' is due to the

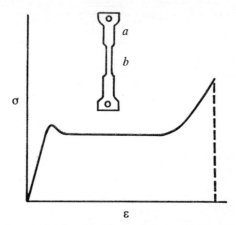

FIG. 1.15 Stress-strain curve in cold drawing.
Inset is the appearance of the test-piece itself,
(a) undrawn (b) drawn regions respectively.

reduction of configurational entropy occasioned by this elongation rather than to internal energy changes. These ideas have been used to predict quantitatively the form of the stress-strain curve and, providing strain does not induce crystallisation, the predictions are quite accurate. A full treatment of this subject can be found else-where.[1]

(ii) *Behaviour of the elastic modulus*

Most investigations of the mechanical properties of polymers employ strains sufficiently small to allow the deformation process to be characterized by one of the Hookean moduli discussed above. The behaviour of the elastic moduli (E and G are the most commonly considered) has been studied as a function of time and temperature for a wide variety of polymers and some such results have already been discussed in considering the glass transition in amorphous polymers. We now deal briefly with some other aspects of this behaviour.

(a) *Creep and stress relaxation.* It was stated above that the low-strain elastic moduli of polymers are functions of the rate of test as well as of temperature. This time-dependence of the moduli gives rise to the phenomena of creep and stress relaxation. Creep is the increase of strain with time observed in a specimen under constant stress and, conversely, stress-relaxation is the decrease of stress with time at constant strain. Thus, in creep

$$\varepsilon(t) = \sigma J(t)$$

and in stress relaxation

$$\sigma(t) = \varepsilon G(t)$$

$$\left.\right\} \text{but } J(t) \neq \frac{1}{G(t)}$$

A typical creep curve, showing also the slow recovery which follows the removal of the stress, is given in Fig. 1.16 where $\varepsilon(t)$ is plotted as

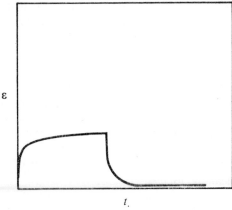

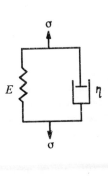

FIG. 1.16 Creep and recovery curves produced by sudden application of a load and its sudden removal after a period of time.

FIG. 1.17 Kelvin spring and dashpot element.

a function of time for a constant stress applied for a time t_1 and then suddenly removed. This behaviour can be qualitatively imitated by a mechanical model consisting of an elastic spring and a viscous 'dashpot' in parallel as shown in Fig. 1.17. This arrangement is known as a Kelvin element. If a constant load is applied the deformation of the element increases with time at a rate governed by the dashpot until the applied load is balanced completely by the restoring force in the spring. If the strain in the element at any time is ε, the stress, which is the sum of the stresses in the two parts of the element, must be

$$\sigma = \eta\dot{\varepsilon} + E\varepsilon$$

where η is the viscosity coefficient of the dashpot and E the Youngs modulus of the spring. The solution of this equation gives

$$\varepsilon = \frac{\sigma}{E}(1 - \exp(-Et/\eta)). \tag{1.13}$$

The quantity η/E has the dimension of time and is called the retardation time of the model. Equation (1.13) can be rewritten

$$\varepsilon(t) = \varepsilon(\infty)\{1 - e^{-t/\tau}\}. \tag{1.14}$$

Clearly the strain in such an element rises asymptotically to its final value at a rate governed by τ. The Kelvin model, though qualitatively instructive, is not a good approximation to a real polymer and more complicated models have been proposed. Satisfactory agreement is only really achieved when a material is represented by an infinite series of such elements with retardation times τ_1, τ_2, τ_3, . . . , τ_∞. The relative weight w allowed to each model (or each value of τ) is then characterised by means of a spectrum of retardation times: a graph of $w(\tau)$ plotted as a function of τ and derived, of course, empirically. Once this spectrum is known it is possible, in principle at least, to predict the creep or stress relaxation behaviour at any stress level (providing different deformation mechanisms do not intrude) and at any time. If all retardation times depend upon temperature in the same way and if the nature of this dependence is known, behaviour at different temperatures can also be predicted.

(b) *Alternative treatment for oscillatory tests.* In order to define clearly the rate parameter in mechanical tests it is common to employ an oscillating load applied to the specimen at a given frequency. This necessitates a redefinition of elastic modulus for the following reason. Suppose the applied stress varies with time in a sinusoidal manner,

$$\sigma = \sigma_0 \sin \omega t \tag{1.15}$$

where ω is the angular frequency (i.e., 2π times the frequency). Provided behaviour is Hookean the strain will also vary sinusoidally

$$\varepsilon = \varepsilon_0 \sin \omega t. \tag{1.16}$$

Equation (1.16) however only applies if no energy is dissipated as heat and the retraction curve coincides with the extension curve as shown in Fig. 1.18(a). Most polymers are not ideal and energy is dissipated during a stress-strain cycle which thus assumes the form shown in Fig. 1.18(b). In this case the maximum strain no longer

occurs at the maximum stress, i.e., the stress and strain are no longer
in phase. We must therefore write

$$\varepsilon = \varepsilon_0 \sin (\omega t - \delta) \qquad (1.17)$$

where δ is the 'phase angle'. A consequence of this phase difference is

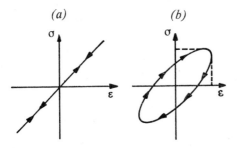

Fig. 1.18   Stress-strain cycles in (a) an ideal and
(b) a visco-elastic solid.

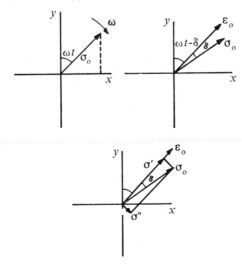

Fig. 1.19

that we cannot define a modulus as the instantaneous ratio of stress
to strain since this ratio varies from $+\infty$ to $-\infty$ according to the
time at which the ratio is calculated.

The solution of these difficulties is best explained diagrammatically.
Suppose a line of length σ_0 has one end fixed at the origin of a set of
cartesian co-ordinates and revolves as indicated in Fig. 1.19 at an

angular velocity ω. Then the projection of this line on the x-axis at a time t is $\sigma_0 \sin \omega t$, that is σ, the stress at that time. Similarly a line of length ε_0 following the first line at a constant angular separation δ has a projection $\varepsilon_0 \sin (\omega t - \delta)$ or simply ε on the x-axis. Now suppose the vector σ_0 is resolved into two components, $(\sigma_0 \cos \delta)$ in phase with the strain vector ε_0 and $(\sigma_0 \sin \delta)$ 90 degrees out of phase and let

$$\left. \begin{array}{l} \sigma_0 \cos \delta \equiv \sigma' \\ \sigma_0 \sin \delta \equiv \sigma'' \end{array} \right\} \tag{1.18}$$

It is now possible to define 'dynamic moduli'

$$\left. \begin{array}{l} E' = \sigma'/\varepsilon_0 = E^* \cos \delta \\ E'' = \sigma''/\varepsilon_0 = E^* \sin \delta \end{array} \right\} \tag{1.19}$$

where $E^* = \sigma_0/\varepsilon_0$, and it follows that

$$E^* = (E'^2 + E''^2)^{\frac{1}{2}} \tag{1.20}$$

and

$$\tan \delta = E''/E. \tag{1.21}$$

The same results can be obtained by supposing the absolute modulus to be a complex quantity,

$$E^* = E' + iE'' \tag{1.22}$$

and for this reason E' and E'' are sometimes called respectively the real and imaginary parts of the modulus. The quantity $\tan \delta$ can be shown to be a measure of the energy dissipated in a single cycle and is simply related to parameters commonly used to characterise this quantity such as logarithmic decrement d,

$$d = \pi \tan \delta \tag{1.23}$$

and rebound resilience R

$$R = \exp(-\pi \tan \delta). \tag{1.24}$$

Because E'' governs the value of $\tan \delta$ (see equation (1.21)) when E' is varying slowly, E'' is often referred to as the loss modulus. The dynamic moduli E' and E'' (equally G' and G'', and so on) provide a full account of a dynamic mechanical experiment in a way that a single modulus could never do and it is usual to quote values for both in any survey of a polymer's low-strain mechanical properties. Some examples are now considered.

Amorphous polymers typically display a large decrease in the real part of the modulus at the glass transition as has already been discussed. This is accompanied by a sharp maximum in the curve of E'' or tan δ as shown in Fig. 1.20 for polystyrene.[9] Like the curves for E' or G' those of E'', G'' or tan δ can be superimposed at temperatures above T_g by use of the WLF transform. When the behaviour of the moduli is considered over the whole temperature range secondary

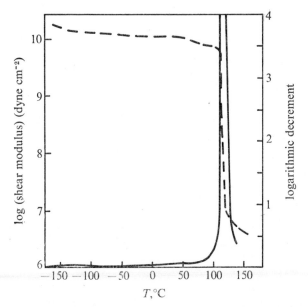

FIG. 1.20 Shear modulus and logarithmic decrement of polystyrene across the glass transition range (after Schmieder and Wolf[9]).

transitions are frequently observed as smaller maxima in the loss modulus or tan δ curves. This can be seen for some amorphous polymers [10] in Fig. 1.21 and for some crystalline polymers in Fig. 1.22 which shows data for three types of nylon.[11] The size of the maxima depend in a complicated fashion upon the degree of branching, the chemical composition of side groups, the degree of crystallinity, the amount of moisture in the specimen and so on. In all cases, however, secondary transitions can be said to arise from the limited motion of molecular segments and in some cases the particular motion responsible for a transition has been identified.

The general effect of crystallinity on the glass transition is to broaden its temperature range, to lessen the overall decrease in real modulus and to reduce the loss modulus maximum. These effects

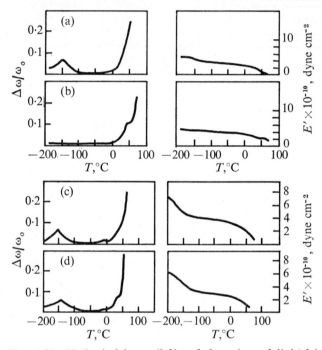

FIG. 1.21 Mechanical losses (*left*) and dynamic moduli (*right*) showing secondary transitions in some amorphous polymers. (a) poly-n-propyl methacrylate; (b) polyisopropyl methacrylate; (c) polypropyl α-chloroacrylate; (d) poly-n-butyl α-chloroacrylate (after Hoff, Robinson and Willbourne[10]).

can be interpreted as arising from the varying degrees of constraint imposed upon the amorphous regions by the presence of crystalline material since the glass transition (unlike some secondary transitions) occurs only in the amorphous phase.

(iii) *Mechanical hysteresis at large strains*

The dissipation of energy as heat in a stress-strain cycle constitutes the phenomenon of mechanical hysteresis. This has already been considered in the previous section for small strains, being measured by the quantity tan δ, but it occurs to a far greater extent at high strains and, since fracture is a high-strain phenomenon, exerts considerable influence upon the processes which concern us in this book. When, for instance, a crack propagates through a material to produce fracture every element of the body close to the crack path experiences a full stress-strain cycle as the crack (with its associated

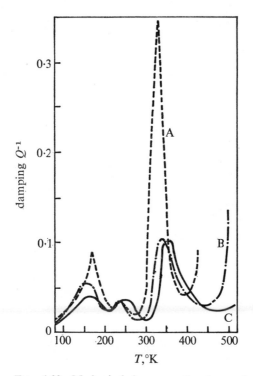

FIG. 1.22 Mechanical losses as functions of temperature for three types of nylon. (A) nylon copolymer, (B) nylon 6-10, (C) nylon 6-6 (after Woodward *et al.*[11]).

region of high stress) approaches and recedes from it. Very close to the crack path this cycle will be a high-strain cycle, and the presence and severity of mechanical hysteresis will undoubtedly affect the propagation of the crack.[12]

Strictly speaking the term mechanical hysteresis applies when the deformed specimen resumes its original shape after removal of the load. A good example of this is a gum (i.e., unfilled) rubber which

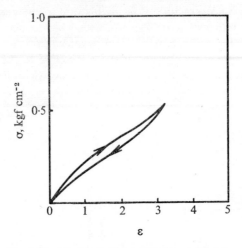

FIG. 1.23   Mechanical hysteresis in a gum rubber.

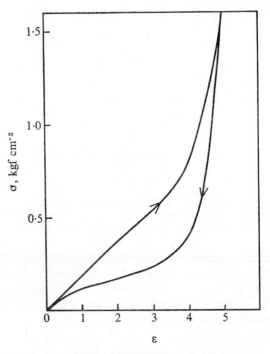

FIG. 1.24   Mechanical hysteresis in a strain-crystallising
rubber.

may behave as shown in Fig. 1.23. If strain-induced crystallisation occurs a much larger amount of energy will be dissipated as indicated in Fig. 1.24.

Filled rubbers and most plastics exhibit a residual strain after removal of the load, even when the maximum strain in the cycle is small or well below the yield strain (Fig. 1.25). This residual strain or 'set' is often recovered, however, after the passage of time and

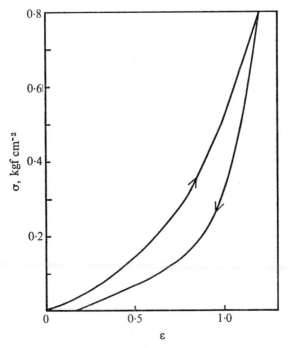

FIG. 1.25 Mechanical hysteresis and 'set' in a filled rubber.

especially if the temperature is raised. Even large (post-yield) strains which remain on removal of the load and which appear to be plastic or irrecoverable in nature are frequently recovered if the temperature is raised. Because of these facts it is not easy in polymers to differentiate between true mechanical hysteresis and the dissipation of energy by plastic flow. The distinction is fortunately of secondary importance in the subject of fracture since the significant phenomenon is the dissipation of energy during a stress cycle and this occurs in both hysteresial and plastic behaviour.

The proportion of energy dissipated is dependent upon several things. The nature of the material and the maximum strain achieved in the cycle are, of course, important. In many cases the rate and the temperature of test are also determining factors. Generally speaking, the faster the stress-strain cycle or the lower the temperature, the higher will be the proportion of energy dissipated,[15] though hysteresis in elastomers due to strain-crystallisation or fillers does not conform to this simple rule. This rate and temperature dependence of hysteresial or plastic dissipation accounts for much of the rate and temperature dependence of fracture phenomena in polymers.

1.6 MICROSTRUCTURE OF POLYMERS

(i) *Forms of microstructure*

The microstructure of a material is its physical structure or texture on a microscopic (including electron-microscopic) scale. Few materials are found to be physically homogeneous when studied under the light or electron microscope although the nature of their heterogeneity varies widely. The common forms of heterogeneity in solids can be classified as follows:

(*a*) *Flaws or defects.* These occur in all solids and may represent the only departure from homogeneity in an otherwise uniform material. Examples are microcracks in glassy materials and dislocations or impurity clusters in otherwise perfect single crystals. This form of microstructure, although perhaps the most elementary, exerts a profound influence over fracture and yield phenomena.

(*b*) *Phase separation in chemically homogeneous materials.* Even if chemical homogeneity exists in a solid the latter may remain physically heterogeneous. This usually occurs when the atoms or molecules composing the material possess crystalline order in some regions but not in others. In metals and crystalline ceramics non-crystallinity is limited to the narrow regions which constitute grain boundaries and accounts for less than 1 per cent of the total material present. Nevertheless the presence of these disordered regions has a profound influence on the mechanical properties of a solid. In solid polymers the percentage of disordered or amorphous material is many times greater and the 'degree of crystallinity' ranges from zero (in some glassy plastics and elastomers) to 98 per cent in some isotactic

Fig. 1.26   Phase separation in a 90/10 blend of natural rubber and ethylene-propylene rubber, the latter showing white. Electron micrograph of an ultra-thin section. Magnification 20 000.

polymers. Further, the degree of crystallinity can vary in the same polymer sample according to its thermal history and the ambient temperature. The internal organisation of the amorphous and crystalline phases will be considered presently.

(c) *Phase separation in chemically heterogeneous materials.* Any system containing more than one chemical species may minimise its free energy by precipitation of one of them, i.e., by phase separation. Complete solid-solution is uncommon but such solutions may exist partially even when phase separation occurs. Metallic alloys are of course examples of systems in which both solid solution and phase separation occur, the phases generally consisting not of the parent metals themselves but of a variety of chemically stable compounds. In polymers phase separation is encountered chiefly in blends or graft polymers and involves the straightforward incompatability of the two parent polymeric species (see Fig. 1.26).

(d) *Fillers or reinforcing agents.* Composite solids, consisting of physical mixtures of unlike components, have been produced in an attempt to improve the basic properties of the parent materials. Examples include cermets, in which a metallic matrix is hardened and made resistant to creep by the inclusion of high-melting ceramic powders, and the 'fillers' and pigments frequently mixed into polymeric materials. In some cases, such as that of carbon black in rubber for example, spectacular improvements of strength have been obtained. A further method of reinforcement involves the use of fibres to strengthen a metallic or polymeric matrix and improvements in stiffness and creep resistance are frequently obtained. 'Fibre-glass', consisting of glass fibres in a matrix of thermosetting polymer, is the commonest example of such a material.

(ii) *Crystalline-amorphous textures in polymers*

Although some important polymers are amorphous, possessing no intrinsic microstructure on a scale higher than the molecular, most commercial plastics are semi-crystalline as outlined above. We now consider briefly the organisation of the crystalline and amorphous components within the solid.

If a polymer which is capable of crystallising is taken up into dilute solution and allowed to precipitate by slow cooling, it may do so in the form of single crystals a few microns across. These single crystals are usually platelets or lamellae with a thickness of only a few hundred Angstrom units and with the long chain molecules folded back and forth through the thickness of the lamella as sketched in Fig. 1.27. Lamellae are often stacked one on top of another and sometimes spiral lamellar terraces are generated, but the basic lamellar character of the crystals is always maintained. The lamellar thickness is a function of temperature of precipitation [14] (see Fig. 1.28) and various theories have been advanced to account for this in terms of the kinetics and thermodynamics of crystallisation.

If the same polymer is crystallised from a molten state, instead of from solution, complete crystallisation is never obtained, a proportion of the solid retaining a liquid or amorphous structure. This can undoubtedly be attributed to the low mobility of the molecules in a

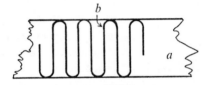

FIG. 1.27 (a) Polymer crystal lamella (b) folded chain molecule.

viscous polymer melt compared with those in dilute solution. Lengthy annealing of the melt-crystallised material may increase the degree of crystallinity but never eliminates the amorphous phase completely.

When examined under a microscope the melt-crystallised polymer is usually found to possess a kind of grain structure, i.e., regions, typically several microns across, are clearly divided from one another by narrow boundaries. The growth of these 'grains' can be watched and, as in a polycrystalline metal, each is observed to nucleate at a point and to grow until its boundaries impinge upon those of neighbouring 'grains'. Here, however, the analogy between metallic and polymeric 'grain growth' breaks down since in a polymer the individual 'grain' is not a single crystal but a composite body consisting of radiating fibrillar or lamellar crystals with interspersed amorphous material. Because of this difference the polymer 'grain' is referred to as a 'spherulite' and will be so named in all that follows.

The detailed structure of spherulites varies from one material to another and also with thermal history, but in all cases the long chain molecules lie tangentially, i.e., perpendicular to the radiating fibrils or lamellae.[15] Since these lamellae and fibrils are well-defined and regular as regards their thickness it is difficult to avoid the conclusion that, like solution-grown single crystals, they also consist of folded molecules and this would automatically account for the tangential orientation of the molecular axis.

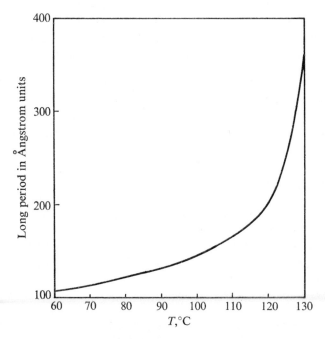

FIG. 1.28 Crystal lamellar thickness in polyethylene, determined by X-ray measurements, as a function of crystallisation temperature (after Geil[14]).

Further evidence is available to show that the lamellae in melt-crystallised polymers are similar in nature to solution-grown single crystals. Disintegration of solid specimens either mechanically or by attack with nitric acid (which preferentially dissolves the amorphous regions) releases single-crystal lamellae which can be studied in the electron microscope and turn out to be essentially similar to their solution grown counterpart, with the molecular axis normal to the lamellar surface.[16] In some specimens the lamellae possess a propellor-like twist and this manifests itself in so-called 'banded' spherulites

where the radiating fibrils or lamellae display a regular helical twist
which gives rise to a concentric pattern of bands when viewed under
certain conditions in the light or electron microscopes.

(iii) *Crystallisation under strain*

Spherulites are not always found in melt-crystallised polymers and
this is usually because crystallisation has occurred under conditions
of strain. Such strain can be set up accidentally, e.g., by mould-flow,
or intentionally as in the production of synthetic fibres. The changes
in crystalline-amorphous texture resulting from crystallisation under
strain have been well documented for the case of natural rubber
(cis-polyisoprene).[17] As strain increases the spherulitic microstructure
gradually gives way to a fibrillar or lamellar texture running perpendicular to the strain direction. This is consistent with orientation of the
molecules along the direction of strain since the molecular axis is then
at right angles to the plane of the lamellae. With further increasing
strain the density of crystal nucleation rises until all the available
space is taken up by nuclei no larger than about 200 Å across. These
nuclei, however, tend to be arranged in strings running along the
direction of strain and these strings impart a longitudinal fibrous
texture to the material.

These textural changes are not the only effect of strain on crystallisation. It has been found that strain also affects both the rate of
crystallisation and the melting temperature of the crystalline phase.
Briefly stated, the effect of increased strain is to accelerate the
crystallisation process and, in natural rubber at least, this is due to an
increased rate of nucleation.[17,18] Increasing strain similarly increases
the melting temperature T_m of the crystals, as is to be expected since

$$T_m = \Delta H_m / \Delta S_m$$

where ΔH_m and ΔS_m are the heat and entropy of fusion respectively.
If melting involves the transition of molecules from an ordered
crystalline array to a semi-ordered (i.e., strained) amorphous condition the configurational entropy change will be much smaller than
when the amorphous phase is randomly ordered. Under strain,
therefore, ΔS_m is smaller and T_m is accordingly larger.

These effects give rise to the phenomenon of strain-induced crystallisation in some elastomers. As the strain at, say, 20°C is increased a
point is reached at which T_m attains this ambient value and crystallisation is observed. Since the nucleation density is a function of

strain [17] the degree of crystallinity continues to increase as the strain rises beyond this critical point until a saturation value (in natural rubber about 30 per cent crystallinity) is achieved. Strain induced crystallinity is important in fracture since it imparts both stiffness and strength, and because at least some part of a body must pass through this strain-crystallised condition before fracture occurs in such materials.

(iv) *Microstructure and fracture*

The effect of microstructure upon fracture behaviour is taken up in Chapter 3 but the importance of the subject cannot be overstressed. Some understanding has been achieved of the way in which filler or fibre reinforcement affects strength in polymers but the role of crystalline texture is still poorly defined and this is why special attention has been given to this form of microstructure in the foregoing discussion. The role of flaws is considered further, not only in Chapter 3 but also in the theoretical development of the subject in Chapters 4 and 5.

References

1. TRELOAR, L. R. G. *The Physics of Rubber Elasticity*, O.U.P., London (1958).
2. SAUNDERS, D. W. *Trans. Faraday Soc.*, **53**, 860 (1957).
3. TOBOLSKY, A. V. *Rheology* (Ed. F. R. Eirich), Vol. 2, p. 63, Academic Press, N.Y. (1958).
4. KOVACS, A. *J. Polym. Sci.*, **30**, 131 (1958).
5. FERRY, J. D. *Viscoelastic Properties of Polymers*, p. 226, John Wiley and Sons, Inc. (1961).
6. WILLIAMS, M. L., LANDEL, R. F., and FERRY, J. D. *J. Am. chem. Soc.*, **77**, 3701 (1955).
7. FERRY, J. D. *Viscoelastic Properties of Polymers*, p. 224, John Wiley and Sons Inc. (1961).
8. FITZGERALD, E. R., GRANDINE, L. D., and FERRY, J. D. *J. appl. Phys.*, **24**, 650 (1953).
9. SCHMIEDER, K., and WOLF, K. *Kolloid-Zeit.*, **134**, 149 (1953).
10. HOFF, E. A. W., ROBINSON, D. W., and WILLBOURNE, A. H. *J. Polym. Sci.* **18**, 161 (1955).

4

11. WOODWARD, A. E., *et al. J. Colloid Sci.*, **12**, 363 (1957).
12. ANDREWS, E. H. *J. Mech. Phys. Solids*, **11**, 231 (1963).
13. SCHALLAMACH, A., *et al. Br. J. appl. Phys.*, **16**, 241 (1965).
14. GEIL, P. H. *Polymer Single Crystals*, p. 88, Interscience Publishers (1963).
15. GEIL, P. H. *Polymer Single Crystals*, p. 228, Interscience Publishers (1963).
16. PALMER, R. P., and COBBOLD, A. J. *Makromol. Chem.*, **74**, 174 (1964).
17. ANDREWS, E. H. *Proc. R. Soc.*, *A*, **277**, 562 (1964).
18. GENT, A. N. *Trans Faraday Soc.*, **50**, 521 (1954).

CHAPTER 2

Fracture Phenomena in Polymers I

2.1 FRACTURE

We must begin by defining the term 'fracture' itself. By fracture we mean the creation of new surfaces within a body. This definition though simple, is really very comprehensive and could be applied equally well to a liquid mass as to a solid body, embracing such phenomena as cavitation and the 'melt fracture' of visco-elastic liquids. For our purposes, however, the definition will be applied to solids only, using the term 'solid' in its mechanical sense. The definition as it stands does not specify how the creation of new surfaces is effected and we might wish to add the words 'by the application of external forces'. This is generally true but it would exclude such phenomena as fracture due to electrical breakdown of the solid, thermal fatigue and so on which involve the setting up of *internal* stresses which overcome the cohesive forces within the material. Corrosion cracking is another case in point since here the energy for rupture is provided partly by a chemical reaction. It is safer, therefore, to take our definition as it stands since, as we shall see, even fracture produced by external loading of a body is not in general independent of thermal processes within the solid.

Other words are often used synonomously with 'fracture'. Of these the term 'rupture' may be regarded as truly synonomous but not the term 'failure' since the latter indicates only that some change has taken place in the body (generally an engineering component of some kind) which renders it unsuitable for its intended use. Fracture is only one of many possible modes of failure, others being creep deformation and plastic flow which in themselves do not involve the creation of new surfaces and so do not constitute fracture (though they may ultimately lead to it). On the other hand a term such as 'cracking' whilst clearly involving fracture is more limited than the latter since there are other modes of fracture which cannot be described in this way. In fact the greatest value of the definition given here is that it helps to unify a wide range of phenomena that we might otherwise think are quite independent, such as the tensile fracture of a brittle solid like glass and the tearing of a plastic film.

The creation of new surfaces involves the supply of energy, the so-called surface energy of the material. This energy is half that required to separate unit area of one layer of atoms or molecules in the substance from the neighbouring layer and to remove the surfaces so formed to an infinite distance apart. (The factor of a half occurs because there are two surfaces each of unit area.) Since the forces between atoms are short range, extending their influence at the most to a few atomic radii, effectively all of this energy is expended in separating the two layers by a distance of this minute order. This process is simple to envisage in a perfect crystal where the separating layers of atoms may be thought of as the layers above and below a cleavage plane. It is less easy to picture what happens in an amorphous polymer where there is no ordered lattice and the creation of surfaces within the body may involve the pulling-out of long lengths of chain molecule, but the energy required in the latter case will not exceed the surface energy of a co-valently bonded crystal, since any pulling-out must necessarily require less energy than the rupture of the co-valent bonds which hold the molecular chain intact. A further factor is that there will always be fewer co-valent bonds crossing unit area in an amorphous solid than in a crystal because of poorer atomic packing. In a single crystal the surface energy is a function of crystallographic direction and of temperature; in an amorphous polymer it may depend upon temperature and also upon the rate of creation of the surfaces because the pulling-out of molecules will be governed by rate. A polymer consisting of both crystalline and amorphous phases may behave in an intermediate manner, though fracture may tend to occur through the amorphous material and if this happens the resultant surface energy will be that of the non-crystalline phase. As we shall see later the creation of new surfaces by fracture generally requires energy to be supplied in excess of the surface energy itself. This extra energy is lost as heat, sound or as the kinetic energy of the fractured body. The surface energy, however, is the *minimum* energy required for the creation of new surfaces.

2.2 Modes of Fracture

The definition of fracture given tells us what fracture is. If we now begin to specify the conditions under which it occurs we find that a variety of different 'modes of fracture' are encountered. For example, if we take a rod of material and subject it to increasing tensile load until it breaks we say that we have caused a tensile fracture. We may go further to examine the broken ends of the rod and decide whether any significant amount or plastic flow preceded fracture and whether the fracture surface itself is 'fibrous' or smooth. On the basis of this examination we may term the fracture 'ductile' or 'brittle' according to whether appreciable plastic flow has or has not taken place. In this book we shall however seek to avoid confusion by keeping the term 'mode of fracture' to describe *the conditions under which fracture occurs*, these conditions being chiefly those of stress and environment. Thus ductile and brittle fracture will be regarded as different behaviours of the fracture itself but may both occur in the tensile mode of fracture.

To go one step further, tensile fracture is itself only one kind of fracture caused by direct mechanical loading of a body till it fails. We could instead apply a compressive stress to crush the material or a bending moment to break it in flexure. There is clearly no limit to the possible stress systems under which fracture can be made to occur and we shall therefore include all such fractures under the general title of 'fracture under direct loading'. This is discussed in detail below.

Our second mode of fracture is 'crack propagation'. Here the conditions of stress differ from those of 'direct loading' in that the spread of a crack in the body is made observable by controlling the stress system to avoid the crack 'running away' or propagating catastrophically. A simple example of this is the action of tearing, in which we are usually able to control the length of tear at will by limiting the supply of energy. Other examples of crack propagation are the cracking of brittle materials like glass or hard polymers and the cleavage of a crystal. Of course the distinction between very rapid crack propagation and fracture under direct loading is not clear-cut and the two modes of fracture do not differ in any absolute sense. In so far, however, as crack propagation involves more or less controlled spreading of fracture and direct-loading fracture involves uncontrolled or catastrophic events, the distinction is both convenient and important.

A third mode of fracture is that of fatigue. In this case the material is subjected to conditions of alternating stress, and fractures after a large number of loading cycles even though the maximum stress applied during the cycle may be far smaller than would be required to produce fracture under direct loading. The process of fatigue is known to involve the creation and incremental propagation of small flaws or cracks until they achieve macroscopic proportions and the specimen fractures.

The fourth fracture mode is creep fracture, sometimes called 'static fatigue'. This is the phenomenon in which fracture occurs some time after the application to the body of a constant load or system of stresses. It differs from fracture under direct loading in that the stress in the body remains constant after application whereas in 'direct loading' the stress is increased continuously until fracture is produced. Many materials, including glass and polymeric solids exhibit a well defined relation between the (steady) applied stress and the time to fracture and this phenomenon shows that the resistance to fracture and consequently the strength of many substances is a time-dependent quantity; the greater the time allowed the lower the stress required to produce fracture. Creep fracture is itself a function of temperature, occurring sooner at high temperatures than at low ones and we must therefore recognise that fracture phenomena are often dependent upon the environmental conditions as well as the time-scale on which they are observed. It is clear that the phenomenon of creep fracture must play a part even in fracture under direct loading since it leads us to expect a time-scale effect in the latter mode. If direct loading is applied very rapidly and fracture is achieved over a very small interval of time we would expect higher stresses to be attained prior to fracture than if the experiment were carried out slowly. This is found to be the case for polymeric materials so that once again our various modes of fracture must be seen as convenient sub-divisions of a single process rather than absolutely distinguishable phenomena.

A fifth fracture mode is wear or abrasion. The inclusion of this process under the heading of fracture may appear strange at first and it is true that wear is seldom a pure fracture phenomenon. Fracture does, however, contribute greatly to the process in that small particles of the material are torn or broken off the wearing surface. This is the predominant process in the wear of rubber which is therefore almost entirely a fracture-based phenomenon. The conditions under which fracture occurs are, in this case, conditions of small geometrical scale, high speed and, probably, high temperature. It is the high temperature condition, brought about by frictional heating, that complicates the wear process in many materials. If sufficient heat is generated to cause local melting, thermal degradation or chemical reaction (chiefly oxidation), it is plainly impossible to describe wear simply as a fracture phenomenon, but fracture is nevertheless an important part of what goes on when surfaces abrade and a knowledge of the simpler modes of fracture will therefore throw light upon the wear process.

The sixth and final mode of fracture that we shall consider is environmental (or corrosion) stress cracking. This is a phenomenon encountered in metals, glass and polymers in which the material fractures under comparatively small, steady stresses when exposed to a corrosive or chemically active environment. It does not follow, of course, that the process is the same in different classes of materials. In metals, for example, the corrosion mechanism is probably electrochemical whereas in rubber it is purely chemical, but the similarity lies in the fact that the major part of the energy required for fracture is provided by chemical or physical-chemical processes and the applied stress plays a secondary, though essential role. This mode of fracture is of great practical importance since most materials are called upon to function in more or less hostile environments and the failure of engineering components and the deterioration of materials in general are frequently attributable to this cause.

This brief summary of fracture modes serves to indicate the breadth of our subject and it will be impossible in this book to treat in great depth many of the topics touched upon. What will be done is to concentrate on the essentials of the fracture process as defined originally and to illustrate the application of these basic ideas to the wide variety of different phenomena embraced by the six 'modes of fracture' discussed above. We shall discover that a surprising degree of unity can be introduced into the subject by following this plan, the ultimate object being, of course, to describe each fracture event in terms of one basic process occurring under some specific set of conditions.

In this chapter and the next the various modes of fracture will be discussed from an empirical standpoint. The results obtained experimentally when polymeric materials are fractured will be briefly reviewed so that it will be possible to proceed to the more theoretical

discussion which ensues in the remaining chapters with a clear idea of
the phenomena we are seeking to explain.

2.3 FRACTURE UNDER DIRECT LOADING

(i) *Tensile strength*

Of the many different systems of stress that can be applied to a
specimen with the object of causing it to fracture, the simplest
experimentally is a uniaxial tensile load. This has the advantage that
all parts of the specimen, except for the regions close to the grips, are

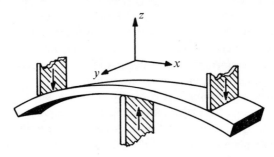

FIG. 2.1   Three point bending test.

under the same conditions of stress both as regards direction and
magnitude so that fracture occurs under well defined conditions. This
only applies of course to a specimen of uniform geometry with
constant cross-sectional area normal to and boundaries parallel to
the applied stress. The fracture stress obtained in such a test is called
the tensile strength of the material and, understandably, most of the
experimental measurements of fracture stress in polymers have been
of this kind.

A variation of this method of testing is the bending test in which a
beam of the material is subjected to three or four point bending
(Fig. 2.1). Here also fracture occurs under a uniaxial stress since on
the free, convex surface of the bent specimen

$$\sigma_x = \sigma; \quad \sigma_y = \sigma_z = 0$$

where the co-ordinate axes x, y and z are as shown in Fig. 2.1. The
difference between a bending test and a tensile test therefore lies not
in the state of stress under which fracture is initiated but in the

localisation of the fracture origin on the convex surface of the specimen. This has the advantage that, since a much smaller volume of the specimen is under high stress, the chance of premature fracture from random flaws is considerably diminished. A further advantage is that gripping the specimen in such a way as to prevent failure at the grips, which is sometimes very difficult in tensile tests, presents no difficulty in bending tests. On the other hand it is necessary in a bending test to calculate the surface stress at which fracture occurs, this being given for three point loading by $\sigma_f = Pl/2bh^2$ where P is the force to cause fracture, l the length of the beam between end supports, and b and h the breadth and thickness of the (rectangular) beam respectively. The stress calculated in this way may be in error for various reasons, including non-Hookean behaviour and deflections larger than allowed for in the theory. It has also been shown that the *spread* of fracture is inhibited in a bent specimen because the region immediately below the surface on which fracture begins is at a lower stress than the surface itself and the *state* of stress there is also more complex.[1] This complication, together with the diminished volume under high stress in the bending test, causes tensile strengths measured in bending to be typically 15–20 per cent higher than those measured in a tensile test. The ratio of the two 'tensile strengths' is called the 'rupture factor' of a material. Since however fracture occurs in both tests under a uniaxial tension we shall not generally differentiate between them.

(ii) *Tensile strength of brittle polymers*

As has already been stated our present purpose is to briefly review the experimental facts before discussing in later chapters the mechanisms of fracture that underlie them. We consider first the brittle fracture of polymers under tensile loading, the term 'brittle' signifying 'without detectable plastic deformation at any point in the specimen'. This type of fracture is observed in some thermosetting resins and in thermoplastics below what is known as the brittle-ductile transition temperature which will be discussed later. In brittle fracture the stress-strain curve is almost linear up to fracture and the strain at fracture is low, of the order of a few per cent. Fig. 2.2 shows ε_f as a function of temperature for a sample of polymethylmethacrylate (PMMA) and Fig. 2.3 a similar curve for polypropylene.[2] The brittle-ductile transition is clearly indicated by a rapid rise in ε_f with increasing temperature above 10°C and −50°C respectively for the two polymers. Apart from the differences in temperature the behaviours of the two polymers are very similar in spite of the fact that the former is completely amorphous and the latter semi-crystalline. The fracture stress or tensile strength in the brittle condition is a function of temperature as indicated in Figs. 2.4 and 2.5 rising as temperature decreases towards a value of some 2800 kgf cm^{-2} for both PMMA and polypropylene at absolute zero.

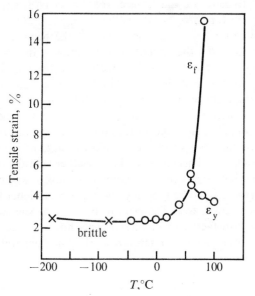

FIG. 2.2 Fracture and yield strains for PMMA as functions of temperature (after Vincent[2]).

Polymers which fracture in a ductile manner at room temperature may also be induced to behave in a brittle fashion by increasing the rate of test. This is indicated by a sharp fall in fracture energy as the strain-rate increases above some critical value (Fig. 2.6).[3] Once brittle behaviour has been achieved the tensile strength at 20°C appears to remain sensibly constant at about 1000 to 1050 kgf cm^{-2} for the chlorinated polyether ('penton') to which Fig. 2.6 refers and similar figures seem to apply for other polymers. It has been suggested that these facts indicate that all polymeric materials possess an ultimate tensile strength in the neighbourhood of 2800 kgf cm^{-2} regardless of chemical composition and that this figure represents the stress necessary to overcome Van der Waal's bonding forces within the polymer. Although, however, this is a reasonable value for the rupture of Van der Waals' bonds, the fact that it is obtained only under conditions of minimum molecular mobility (very low temperatures or extremely high rates) argues against a fracture mechanism in which one chain slips past another during separation of the fracture surfaces. It is much more likely that main-chain (i.e., covalent) bonds are broken in the process and this in theory requires

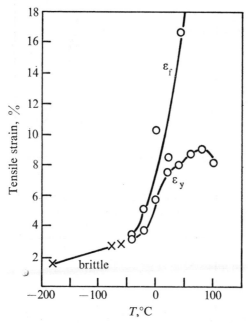

Fig. 2.3   Fracture and yield strains for polypropylene
as functions of temperature (after Vincent[2]).

stresses of the order $E/10$, i.e., about 10^4 kgf cm^{-2} (PMMA at $-200°C$). It seems clear that the experimental tensile strengths fall some way short of the theoretical values but do approach them sufficiently closely in order of magnitude to suggest that a limiting value is in fact being approached under conditions where molecular movement is inhibited. This matter is further discussed in Chapter 4.

Apart from the effects of rate and temperature, the brittle strength of a polymer is greatly influenced by material variables such as molecular weight, crystallinity, additives and cross-linking. Fig. 2.7

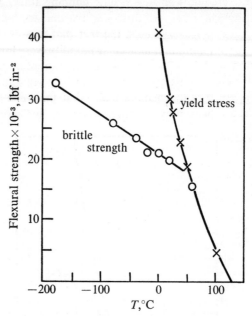

FIG. 2.4   Fracture and yield stresses for PMMA as functions of temperature (after Vincent[2]).

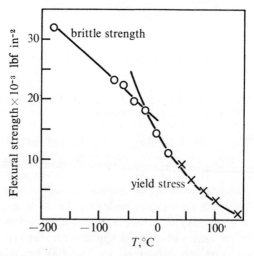

FIG. 2.5   Fracture and yield stresses for polypropylene as functions of temperature (after Vincent[2]).

shows brittle strength plotted against the reciprocal of number-average molecular weight for polythene, PMMA and polystyrene.[4] Clearly brittle strength varies from one polymer to another but also increases rapidly with increased molecular weight with a tendency

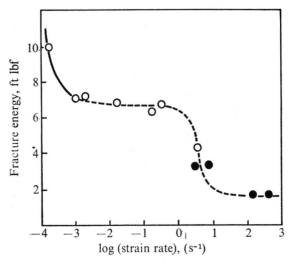

FIG. 2.6   Fracture energy of 'penton' as a function of strain rate. Filled circles represent brittle fracture (after Warburton-Hall and Hazell[3]).

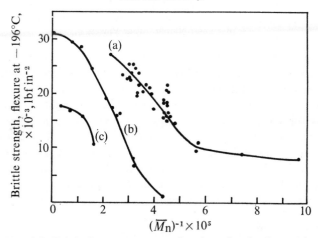

FIG. 2.7   Brittle fracture stress as a function of molecular weight for polyethylene (right), PMMA (centre) and polystryene (left), (after Vincent[4]).

to level off as this becomes very large or very small. At low molecular weight σ_f becomes effectively zero in one amorphous polymer (PMMA) when M_n approaches 25 000 but crystalline materials retain a measure of brittle strength even at a molecular weight of 10 000 or less. At moderate and high molecular weights, on the other hand, crystallinity does not appear to affect the brittle strength greatly, no difference being observed between linear and branched polyethylene in spite of large differences in the degree of crystallinity. This is in

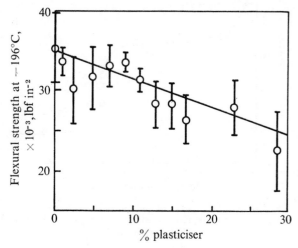

FIG. 2.8   Brittle fracture stress of PVC as a function of plasticiser content (after Vincent[4]).

marked contrast to the strong influence of crystallinity on strength in non-brittle fracture as discussed below, and also does not apply if the material is oriented (see Chapter 3.6).

The effect of plasticiser is to reduce brittle strength, as Fig. 2.8 shows for PVC.[4] The linear reduction with increasing plasticiser suggests that only the polymer molecules carry load in a plasticised material. Cross-linking appears to have little or no effect on brittle strength in PMMA and a relatively small one in natural rubber where the effect may in any case be due to modification of the rubber molecule by the cross-linking agent.

(iii) The brittle-ductile transition

If the temperature of a brittle thermoplastic polymer is increased the stress-strain curve to fracture is likely to change its form, passing through the stages shown in Fig. 2.9. The fracture behaviour ceases to be brittle and becomes ductile, detectable plastic or irreversible strain occurring in the specimen before fracture. The amount of plastic deformation increases rapidly as the temperature rises and may become very large indeed, ε_f rising from one or two per cent under brittle conditions to hundreds of per cent under ductile ones. At the

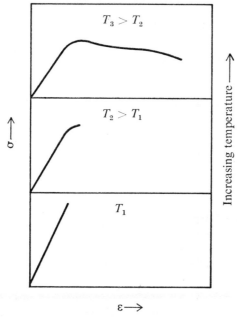

FIG. 2.9 Changes in the stress-strain curve of a brittle thermoplastic with rising temperature (diagrammatic).

same time the appearance of the fracture and of the specimen itself also changes. Under brittle conditions the fracture occurs, typically, perpendicular to the direction of stress, and the broken pieces show no evidence of permanent deformation, but as soon as ductility sets in the fracture path often becomes oblique to this direction suggesting failure by shear.

The change from brittle to ductile behaviour is called the brittle-ductile transition. As was noted earlier, it may be induced not only by changes in temperature but also by changes in the speed of testing, and another way of expressing the dual role of rate and temperature

is to say that the brittle-ductile transition temperature is a function
of rate. Fig. 2.10 shows this dependence for PMMA and PVC over a
limited range of rates.[5] The existence of a brittle-ductile transition
is not limited to polymers and has, in fact, been studied far more
widely in metals. Here also the temperature of transition is affected
by the rate of testing and Fig. 2.10 includes data for zinc and
tungsten as well as the two polymers mentioned.

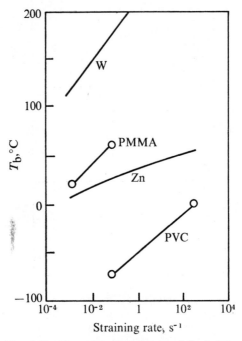

FIG. 2.10   Dependence upon rate of the brittle-
ductile transition temperatures of various solids
(after Vincent[5]).

Information on the effect of rate on the brittle-ductile transition
of polymers is as yet fragmentary but greater detail is available about
the transition itself. Fig. 2.2 shows the transition as it occurs in the
amorphous polymer already cited, PMMA. Below about 10°C the
tensile elongation at fracture is fairly constant at about 2·5 per cent
and the fracture is brittle. The onset of ductility is betrayed by a
sudden upsweep of the curve of fracture strain against temperature
at the transition. It is not easy to quote an exact transition temperature

and it is better to quote a range, say 10–20°C for this polymer. Above the transition there are two points in the stress-strain curve of which we must take note. The first is the yield point which was defined in Chapter 1 and which is important for two reasons. Firstly it indicates the onset of a new mode of deformation, i.e., plastic flow, and by implication the activation of a new molecular mechanism of deformation. Secondly it has great practical importance because it marks the point at which a component would, in practice, fail, i.e., cease to perform its intended function.

The second point which interests us in the stress-strain curve of a ductile material is of course the actual point of fracture of the specimen which may occur at strains greatly in excess of the yield strain. When the strain is large it must be remembered that the nominal stress in the specimen at fracture may be much smaller than the true stress based on the instantaneous cross-section. In Fig. 2.2 it will be seen that above the brittle-ductile transition the fracture strain increases in the range 20–60°C until a true yield point appears in the stress-strain curve at about 4 per cent strain. Thereafter, as the temperature rises still further the yield strain varies little but the fracture strain continues to increase rapidly.

The behaviour of a crystalline thermoplastic is similar to that of the PMMA whilst differing in detail. Fig. 2.3 shows the data for polypropylene which has its brittle-ductile transition (at the strain rate employed) over the range −30 to −40°C. The main influence of crystallinity appears to be the continued increase in the yield strain with increasing temperature above the transition. The brittle-ductile transition is also reflected in the behaviour of the fracture stress as a function of temperature. In Figs. 2.4 and 2.5 the flexural tensile stress at fracture or at yield is plotted against temperature. In the amorphous polymer the brittle strength falls with rising temperature as previously noted. The yield strength, however, falls even more rapidly above the transition temperature. The yield stress can be extrapolated to temperatures below the brittle-ductile transition by measurements in compression where yield, of course, still occurs but brittle fracture is prevented because there is no tensile component in the applied stress. This extrapolation is shown in Fig. 2.4 and suggests that the phenomenon of yield is independent of that of brittle fracture. The effect of crystallinity in Fig. 2.5 is to make the transition less well defined, though a break in the curve of fracture/yield stress against temperature is still evident.

5

A satisfactory explanation of the brittle-ductile transition can be deduced from the fact that the phenomena of brittle fracture and yield appear to be quite independent, at least in a macroscopic sense. The explanation, which has been used in connection with the same effects in metals, is simply that at any temperature the material has both a yield strength and a brittle fracture strength which are independent and which both vary with temperature. The yield strength, however, is much more dependent upon temperature than the brittle strength so that the situation shown schematically in Fig. 2.11

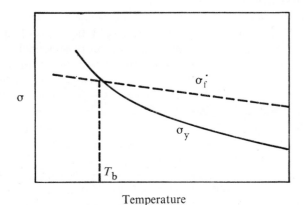

Temperature

FIG. 2.11

obtains. Because of the different temperature dependencies of σ_y and σ_f (brittle) it is likely that at some temperature these two quantities will be equal; below this temperature $\sigma_f < \sigma_y$ and the material will fracture in a brittle manner, whilst above it $\sigma_y < \sigma_f$ (brittle) and fracture will always be ductile.

This concept of independent yield and brittle strengths helps us to understand a number of other features connected with the brittle-ductile transition.[4] For example it explains why the transition occurs near the glass-rubber transition temperature for some polymers but not for others. Around this temperature, it will be remembered, the elastic modulus of a polymer increases rapidly with falling temperature, the magnitude of the change being dependent upon the polymer and its physical state (e.g., crystalline or otherwise), and it has sometimes been supposed that high modulus alone causes a material to be brittle in fracture. This is, however, a fallacy since many polymeric materials are ductile well below their glass-transition and in spite of high initial modulus. Table 2.1 gives T_g and the brittle-ductile transition temperature T_b for normal rates of loading (T_b is, of course, a function of rate of test) for a variety of polymers.

TABLE 2.1

	T_g °C	T_b °C
PMMA	105	45
Polycarbonate of bisphenol A	150	−200
Rigid PVC	74	−20
Natural Rubber	−70	−65
Polystyrene	100	90
Polyisobutylene	−70	−60

The first three materials have $T_b < T_g$ by a considerable margin whilst the latter three have T_b in the region of T_g. It is clear that these two transition temperatures are not necessarily related to each other, and the same objections can be maintained against the view that, in those polymers with more than one modulus transition, the brittle transition is associated with a low-temperature modulus transition. For example, polycarbonate has its lowest modulus transition at −73°C (at 150 c/s) but is ductile down to −196°C in fracture, whilst PTFE with a lowest transition at −93°C (0·6 c/s) is also ductile at −196°C.

The picture thus emerges that T_b and T_g are not simply related but that if the *yield stress σ_y is increasing rapidly in the region of T_g*, as it often does for amorphous polymers, it is likely that σ_y will first exceed σ_f (brittle) in that region and T_b will then be close to T_g. If, on the other hand (for various reasons, e.g., secondary modulus transitions at lower temperatures, or broad glass transitions caused by crystallisation) the yield stress is varying less rapidly with temperature around T_g then T_b is less likely to fall near to T_g. As has already been remarked, metals also display a brittle-ductile fracture transition without undergoing any modulus transitions comparable to those encountered in polymers, so that it is reasonable to expect that the explanation of the fracture transition does not lie in the modulus transition but rather in the independent nature of the yield and brittle strengths.

We must be careful to define what is meant here by 'independent'. These two quantities, σ_y and σ_f (brittle) are independent in the empirical sense that they have different magnitudes and different rates of change with temperature and rate of test. It does not mean that they are unrelated in a causal or mechanistic sense. For instance, it has been shown for metals that brittle fracture is always initiated by some local plastic yielding, which is, however, too small in magnitude to show up in the stress-strain curve. It has further been suggested for metals that below the brittle-ductile transition the yield strength and the brittle strength are identical and that brittle failure is caused at low temperature by the onset of local yield. Reference to Fig. 2.4 will show that this is not the case for polymers (at least not for all polymers) but there is nevertheless a great deal of evidence that brittle fracture in polymers also involves local plastic yielding at the tip of the propagating fracture (see Chapter 5). The *mechanisms* of yield and brittle fracture are likely to be interrelated, therefore, even though the magnitudes of σ_y and σ_f (brittle) apparently vary independently.

(iv) *Yield strength of ductile polymers*

Once a polymer has undergone yield it may either extend to fracture without further increase in load or else it may 'strain harden' and break under a load exceeding the load at yield. Since the cross-sectional area is reduced with increasing strain, the actual stress at the moment of fracture may in the latter case be very much higher than the yield stress. These two forms of behaviour are sketched in Fig. 2.12 and may both occur in the same polymer at different temperatures or strain rates. For a material which does not strain harden, the yield stress is a more important parameter than the fracture stress since once σ_y has been exceeded fracture is certain to ensue in a tensile test. Although, therefore, yield is not a fracture phenomenon as such it is the yield of these materials which determines their resistance to fracture and we shall consider it further.

The tensile yield stress of polymeric solids is, as we have already seen, strongly dependent upon temperature and rises rapidly as the latter falls. It also depends strongly upon the rate of test and Fig. 2.13 indicates the nature and magnitude of this dependence for several polymers. The general behaviour of yield stress as a function of temperature and rate suggests that the yield phenomenon is essentially visco-elastic in nature and this has been precisely confirmed in the case of amorphous polymers. In a series of investigations using PMMA and poly(ethyl methacrylate) Roetling [6] showed that the dependence of tensile yield stress upon temperature and rate of strain (Fig. 2.14) could be described in terms of the Ree-Eyring rate

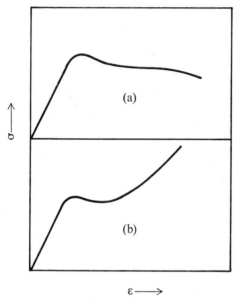

FIG. 2.12 Stress-strain behaviour of ductile polymers (a) without and (b) with strain hardening.

process theory according to which deformation processes are thermally activated. This theory can be regarded as a special case of the more general WLF treatment of visco-elastic behaviour. Roetling found that his data could be expressed in the form

$$\sigma_y/T = \sum_i A_i^{-1} \sinh^{-1} \{(C_i \dot{\varepsilon}/T) \exp (\Delta U_i/RT)\}$$

where $\dot{\varepsilon}$ is the strain rate, ΔU_i the activation energy of the ith segmental-motion process and A_i, C_i are constants. A good fit between experiment and theory (solid lines in Fig. 2.14) could only be obtained if two processes $i_1 = \alpha$ and $i_2 = \beta$ were considered, a single process being insufficient. The relevant constants were

	ΔU_i, kcal mole^{-1}	A_i	$\log_e C_i$
α process	98	23×10^{-6}	-127
β process	32	$9 \cdot 2 \times 10^{-6}$	-38

The theory holds good for PEMA right through the glass transition range (T_g = 65°C), the α process appearing to predominate in the glassy state and the β process at higher temperatures. It is appropriate at this stage to enquire what actually happens, on a molecular level, when a glassy amorphous polymer undergoes yield. Clearly the largest deformations which often follow yield imply an ability on the part of the molecules to uncoil freely as in the rubberlike state.

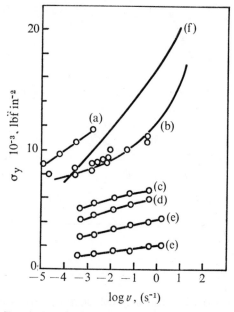

FIG. 2.13   Yield stresses of various polymers as functions of the rate of testing. (a) PMMA, (b) rigid PVC, (c) 'Kralastic' B, (d) polypropylene, (e) polyethylene. Compare (f) copper at 600°C (after Vincent[5]).

The analogy with rubberlike elasticity is strengthened by the fact that most of the 'plastic' deformation is recoverable on heating the specimen indicating that little relative flow of the molecules has occurred. In other words the application of stress to a glassy polymer has much the same effect as raising its temperature to the glass-rubber transition, and it was at one time thought that yield was caused by the generation of heat in the specimen. This latter idea has been proved incorrect and it is clear that stress *alone* is capable of depressing the glass transition so that the phenomenon takes place at the temperature of test when the stress exceeds some particular value.

There are two ways in which this depression of T_g could arise. Firstly the elastic energy stored in a chain molecule may 'assist' the thermal energy of its segments to overcome the energy barriers to main-chain rotations. Secondly the hydrostatic component of the stress system (which component is present even in tensile testing and gives rise to an expansion of the material manifested by a Poisson's

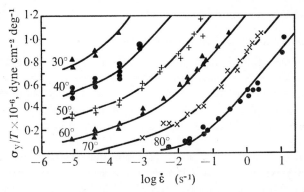

FIG. 2.14 Dependence of yield stress upon temperature and rate of strain for polyethyl methacrylate (after Roetling[6]).

Ratio $\mu < 0.5$) may reduce the actual barriers to rotation by increasing the free volume available to chain segments. Of these two processes the latter might be expected to predominate in the glassy region where μ is a minimum but to have less effect in the rubberlike condition where $\mu \to 0.5$, and it is possible that Roetling's two processes can be identified with these effects. The volume-change mechanism can be shown to be quantitatively significant by considering the known effect of pressure on T_g for polymeric solids. The proportional change in volume $\Delta V/V$ for a material at strain ε is

$$\Delta V / V = \varepsilon(1 - 2\mu)$$

and for a yield strain of 3 per cent and a Poisson's ratio of 0·33 a 1 per cent volume increase is to be expected. According to O'Reilly's data on polyvinyl acetate [7] such a volume change is produced by a hydrostatic tension of about 10^3 atmospheres at 30°C and this corresponds to a change in glass transition temperature of $-21°C$.

This rough calculation serves to indicate the significant magnitude of the volume change effect.

Although semi-crystalline polymers cannot be expected to obey visco-elastic theory the general behaviour of yield stress is similar to that found in amorphous materials. One possible difference is that the tensile strain at yield in crystalline polymers appears to pass through a maximum as the temperature varies, the maximum appearing in polycarbonate at about $-120°C$ ($\varepsilon_y \sim 10$ per cent) and in polypropylene at $80°C$ ($\varepsilon_y \sim 9$ per cent). In amorphous materials the yield strains are generally lower (<5 per cent) and the presence of maxima somewhat uncertain.

(v) *Fracture strength of ductile polymers*

If a polymer strain hardens after yield the fracture stress (especially when reckoned on the final cross-section) exceeds the yield stress and becomes a parameter of importance. It is true of course that the yield point may still dictate the usefulness or otherwise of such a material in engineering applications but this is not necessarily the case. Some materials, like synthetic fibres, exhibit yield of a limited nature and are still employed on account of their high fracture stress. The 'limited yield' in this case is not of the kind which gives rise to irrecoverable deformation but post-yield recovery is often 'delayed'. A second important application of materials above their yield stress is in the field of impact resistance. Since the energy-to-break of a material is given by the integral of force with respect to strain (the area under the force-strain curve), a polymer which strain hardens is potentially capable of withstanding high impact stresses, especially as strain hardening tends to *spread* the area of deformation whilst 'strain softening' tends to localise it. (We saw this in Chapter 1 when discussing cold drawing.)

Strain hardening, with its concomitant of high fracture stress is put to good use when synthetic fibres or polymer films are 'drawn' subsequent to extrusion. A spun filament of 'terylene' (polyethylene terephthalate) for example is only weakly oriented and may be quite brittle. Even better oriented material exhibits cold drawing and therefore large elongation at relatively low stress, though weak strain hardening eventually ensues. If the spun fibre is however stretched by several hundred per cent at a temperature which facilitates uncoiling and crystallisation of the molecules, it becomes a resilient flexible fibre with a tensile strength many times that of the original polymer (even when the latter strength is reckoned on the final cross-section of the specimen). The origin of the high strength of drawn fibres lies in the crystalline anisotropy created by the drawing process and the effect of microstructure on strength is discussed, as far as possible, in Chapter 3.

During post-yield extension the molecules of a polymer become increasingly oriented parallel to the strain axis and as a result the instantaneous elastic modulus must increase rapidly as the molecules reach a fully extended configuration. This occurs in rubberlike elasticity and causes an upsweep of the stress-strain curve which is not predicted on the assumption of infinitely long molecules. Strain hardening is thus to be expected even where no crystallisation is involved. Crystallinity, however, appears to be necessary if any marked effect is to be observed since it provides a 'cross-linking' mechanism which prevents mutual sliding of the oriented molecules and makes the strain hardening less sensitive to the local temperature rise which generally (but not necessarily) accompanies post-yield deformation. In general, therefore, tensile strengths significantly higher than the yield stress are only likely to be observed in ductile polymers when crystallisation is possible. The tensile strengths obtained depend strongly on the conditions of deformation which appear to exert their influence via the perfection or otherwise of the crystalline order achieved before fracture occurs.

(vi) *Tensile strength of elastomers*

Since by definition an elastomer is a material above its glass transition temperature and free (in its unstrained condition) from crystallinity, there is nothing to prevent molecules from slipping past one another to cause fracture at very low stresses except inter-molecular cross-links. It will be remembered that these cross-links may be physical entanglements or chemical 'bridges', the former being effective only for very long molecules and short times of loading. Since these cross-links give rise to a stress-bearing molecular network it is not surprising that the tensile strengths of elastomers are highly dependent both on molecular weight and on the degree of cross-linking and these effects are illustrated in Figs. 2.15 and 2.16.[8,9] Like thermoplastics, elastomers of very low initial molecular weight have little or no tensile strength, but the latter rises rapidly with increasing chain length until it levels off again for a molecular weight which is effectively infinite as far as the fracture mechanism is

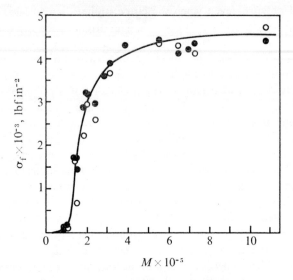

FIG. 2.15 Dependence of tensile strength upon initial molecular weight in pure gum butyl rubber vulcanisates (after Flory[8]).

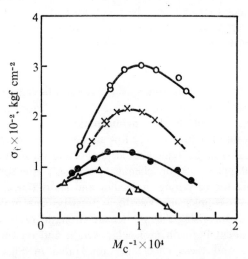

FIG. 2.16 Dependence of tensile strength upon cross-link density in pure gum natural rubber vulcanised respectively with sulphur (○) TMT (×) an organic peroxide (●) and high energy radiation (△) (after Greensmith, Mullins and Thomas[9]).

concerned. There is an important difference between elastomers and thermoplastics, however, in that the tensile strength of an elastomer is a function also of the cross-link density, and it appears that strength begins to increase from zero as soon as there are sufficient cross-links to provide a coherent network. Thus a smaller degree of cross-linking will be required to achieve a given tensile strength in an elastomer having a high initial molecular weight than in one with a lower molecular length. There is naturally a limit to the compensation

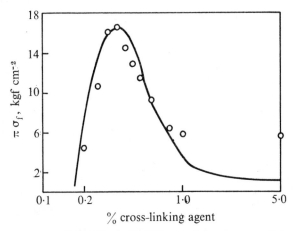

FIG. 2.17   Dependence of tensile strength upon cross-link density in a non-crystallising gum SBR. The solid line is a theoretical curve (after Taylor and Darin[10]).

of low molecular weight by increased cross-linking since as the latter increases the rubber becomes stiffer and its rubberlike nature is eventually destroyed. The dependence [10] of tensile strength on cross-linking density (expressed in terms of the amount of cross-linking agent employed) for a non-crystallising styrene-butadiene rubber is shown explicitly in Fig. 2.17. The solid line is a theoretical curve which will be discussed later and the points are experimental. These results indicate the expected rise of tensile strength with degree of cross-linking as the network is first completed and then strengthened, but also reveals a characteristic fall-off in strength at high cross-link densities which various theories have attempted to explain (see Chapter 5.4).

A profound effect on the tensile strength of some rubbers is exerted by the onset of strain-induced crystallinity above a certain elongation, and it is this phenomenon which imparts high strength to natural rubber (up to 300 kgf cm⁻²) in comparison to say SBR (60 kgf cm⁻²) which does not crystallise. A non-crystallising rubber, however, may have its tensile strength greatly increased by the addition of a suitable filler, such as finely divided silica or carbon black incorporated in proportions up to 30 per cent by weight. Fillers do not appreciably increase the tensile strength of natural rubber so that the originally much weaker synthetic elastomer may

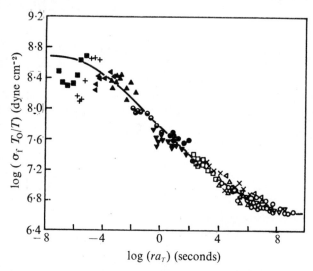

Fig. 2.18   WLF master curve for the dependence of tensile strength upon rate and temperature in gum SBR (after Smith[11]).

be made as strong as the crystallising elastomer if properly compounded. The reason for these effects will be discussed in a later chapter.

So far we have mentioned only the dependence of tensile strength upon elastomer structure, but in common with polymers below their glass transition, rubbers have properties which are strongly rate and temperature dependent. Non-crystallising rubbers are typically far stronger at low temperatures and high rates of strain than under the reverse conditions and their behaviour can be conveniently portrayed by means of the WLF transform (see Chapter 1). The 'master curve' for SBR is shown in Fig. 2.18, where the logarithm of the reduced tensile strength is plotted against the reduced strain rate ra_T.[11] The diagram shows that fracture in non-crystallising elastomers is essentially a visco-elastic process (since otherwise the WLF transform would not work) and also displays neatly the dependence of tensile strength upon the conditions of testing. The temperature dependence is, of course, also implicit in the ordinate since at a given reduced rate the breaking stress is related to T_0/T where T_0 is a reference temperature some 50°C above the glass transition and T is

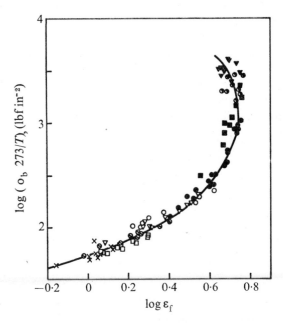

FIG. 2.19 The failure envelope for SBR. The different symbols refer to different temperatures in the range −45 to 140°C (after Smith[12]).

the (absolute) temperature of test. The fracture strain for the same material passes through a maximum at intermediate strain rates reducing to very low values at low speeds (compare Chapter 3 on creep fracture) and at very high rates of testing.

The relation between fracture stress and fracture strain can also be concisely portrayed using the reduced-variable method of plotting experimental data. If the quantity $\log(\sigma_f/T)$ is plotted against $\log \varepsilon_f$ for a non-crystallising elastomer a single curve is obtained (Fig. 2.19) for all rates and temperatures of test.[12] Smith has called this curve the 'failure envelope'. Different degrees of cross-linking give different curves but these can all be superimposed if log ε_f is replaced by log $(E\varepsilon_f/T)$ where E is the initial Young's modulus for the material. This 'master' envelope, like the WLF curve for fracture stress, has the advantage of characterising the polymer itself, being independent of the conditions of test and of cross-linking. It should thus facilitate the comparison of different polymers and it is, in fact, found that many polymers have very similar 'master' envelopes suggesting that the fracture process is not primarily dependent on the particular chemical structure of the molecules.

Crystallising rubbers, such as natural rubber, butyl rubber and neoprene do not display such a marked dependence on temperature and rate, tensile strength varying little over a wide range of temperature from about $-50°$ to about $+100°C$ in the case of natural rubber, and the WLF transform does not apply. However at high speeds and low temperatures of testing, where crystallinity may have insufficient time to develop before fracture, the tensile strengths of crystallising rubbers fall to values similar to those of non-crystallising materials tested under the same conditions.

(vii) *Fracture under bi- and triaxial stress systems*

Our discussion of fracture under direct stress has so far been limited to uniaxial tensile stress systems and we must briefly consider other situations in which there are two or three non-zero principal stresses. Unfortunately there is very little available information on the behaviour of plastics and rubbers under these conditions, not because they are unimportant but because they are more difficult to achieve experimentally than uniaxial loading. In practice fracture usually takes place under complex stress conditions, one important case being that of crack propagation in which a three-dimensional stress field exists at the crack tip.

A great deal of work has been carried out on metals with a view to predicting their yield and fracture behaviour under general systems of stress from that observed under uniaxial stress, and various criteria have been advanced for yield.[13] According to the maximum shear stress criterion yielding takes place when the maximum shear component of the stress field reaches a critical value, the shear strength of the material. In biaxial tension this is expressed by

$$\tfrac{1}{2}(\sigma_1 - \sigma_2) = \tau(\text{critical}).$$

An alternative criterion, the maximum energy theory, takes the following form for biaxial tension

$$\sigma_1^2 + \sigma_2^2 - 2\mu\sigma_1\sigma_2 = \tau^2(\text{critical}).$$

The application of these criteria to the yield of plastics can be tested because they predict different values for the quantity

$$(\sigma_C + \sigma_T)/2\sigma_S$$

where σ_C, σ_T and σ_S are the yield stresses of the material respectively in compression, tension and shear. Vincent [14] has enumerated this quantity for a variety of polymeric materials, the results being shown in Table 2.2

TABLE 2.2

	σ_C	σ_T	σ_S	$(\sigma_C + \sigma_T)/2\sigma_S$
PVC (Darvic 110)	9·8	8·3	6·0	1·53
Polythene (Alkathene XRM–32)	2·1	1·6	1·4	1·35
Polypropylene (Propathene GWE–01)	6·3	4·7	4·0	1·39
PTFE (Fluon G.1)	2·1	1·7	1·6	1·19
Nylon (Maranyl A100 (M))	8·9	9·7	5·9	1·59
ABS resin (Kralastic B)	6·2	6·5	3·5	1·83

$$(\text{lbf in}^{-2} \times 10^{-3})$$

The maximum shear criterion predicts a value of 2 in the last column and the maximum energy theory a value of $\sqrt{3}$. The latter is clearly nearer the experimental figures but it cannot be said that either criterion is satisfactory.

As we have seen, yield may or may not lead to fracture so that a criterion for yield, even if found, would not tell the whole story. Furthermore, brittle fracture behaviour in polymers appears to bear little relationship to yield so that our understanding of fracture under general stress conditions is fragmentary in the extreme. A few results, again obtained by Vincent, are available on brittle fracture under biaxial stress. The biaxial flexural strengths of three methacrylate thermoplastics are compared below with their uniaxial strengths, and the former appear to be consistently higher.

		'Perspex'	Diakon MG	Diakon LG
Flexural strength	Uniaxial	19·8	14·5	16·5
lbf in$^{-2} \times 10^{-3}$	Biaxial	22·6	18·6	22·3

Fracture under full hydrostatic tension has been achieved [15] in thin discs of rubber bonded to circular metal plates which were then pulled in such a manner as to separate the 'sandwich'. Because the rubber layer was thin it was prevented from contracting laterally by the rigid metal plates and failure occurred internally in the centre of the rubber disc under sensibly hydrostatic conditions. The onset of failure was detected as a 'yield point' in the force-deflection curve for the test. Theory predicted a relation between the tensile stress for failure (σ_c) and the corresponding hydrostatic tension for failure (p_c) of the form

$$\sigma_c = \tfrac{1}{2} p_c (1 + 2h^2/a^2)$$

where h is the thickness of the rubber disc and a the radius ($a \gg h$). It was possible also to estimate in terms of p the strain generated at a small, spherical internal flaw, assumed to be present initially and theory indicated that this should become infinite, i.e., inevitably cause failure, when p attained a value of approximately 0·8 of the Young's Modulus of the rubber. Measurements of σ_c for 'sandwiches' of known E, h and a verified these theoretical conclusions.

Although few experimental investigations of fracture under multiaxial stress systems have been carried out there are some general points which may be noted. Firstly an isotropic material cannot yield plastically under a fully hydrostatic tension or compression such as exists in the rubber disc discussed above because there is no component of shear stress in the system. A shear stress is needed to obtain deformation without change in volume, the process that is active in plastic flow. On the other hand a pure shear stress is unlikely to cause brittle fracture since cracks will in general only form when the stresses are tending to increase the volume of the material. In the 'simple' case of uniaxial tensile stress there are, in fact, both hydrostatic components tending to increase the volume and shear components tending to cause flow at some angle to the tensile axis. These considerations alone, therefore, show that the state of stress in the body must affect its fracture behaviour and influence such phenomena as the brittle-ductile transition as well as the fracture stress and strain of the material. As we shall see later this modification of failure properties by the stress system is very important in the case of notch sensitivity and crack propagation where the essentially three dimensional stress system at the root of the notch or crack produces effects different from those obtained in the remainder of the body.

The effect of multiaxial stress is certain to be profound in the ductile failure of those polymers whose crystalline texture changes during the course of testing. These morphological changes depend not only upon the magnitude and speed of straining but also upon the stress system operating at the time. The strain-induced crystallinity of natural rubber, for instance, will be morphologically different in a biaxial tensile test and a uniaxial one, whilst the cold drawing of a polythene specimen will in one case yield a fibrous texture before failure and in the other case a two-dimensionally drawn film.

(viii) *Impact strength*

A body subjected to impact loading may fracture under very different conditions to those obtaining when the same body is loaded in a normal direct-stress test. The possible differences are as follows:

(*a*) Neither the stress nor its rate of application are constant during the test. The stress rises to a maximum which is dependent on the energy and momentum of the impacting mass, the elastic constants

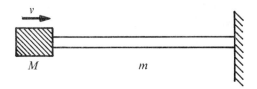

FIG. 2.20

of the specimen and the occurrence or otherwise of inelastic deformation. This maximum stress can only be calculated theoretically for the simplest cases: when the geometry of the specimen is simple, the method of loading is straightforward and the specimen displays Hookean elasticity. Timoshenko [16] has given the solution of this problem for the axial impact loading of a rigidly supported rod of uniform cross-section (Fig. 2.20). The maximum stress is denoted σ_m and the initial stress on impact is denoted σ_0 where $\sigma_0 = v(E\rho)^{\frac{1}{2}}$ v being the velocity of impact, E the Young's modulus of the rod and ρ its density. The ratio (σ_m/σ_0) is found to be a function of the ratio of masses of the impacting body and the rod (M/m) and has the form shown in Fig. 2.21. For comparison Timoshenko gives the values of (σ_m/σ_0) calculated by simply equating the energy of the impacting

6

body to the maximum strain energy in the rod:

$$\tfrac{1}{2}Mv^2 = (\sigma_m^2/2E)(m/\rho)$$

$$\sigma_m = v(M/m)^{\frac{1}{2}}(E\rho)^{\frac{1}{2}}$$

and

$$\sigma_m / \sigma_0 = (M/m)^{\frac{1}{2}}.$$

This result is the lower curve in Fig. 2.21 and can be seen to be seriously in error especially for low values of the parameter (M/m),

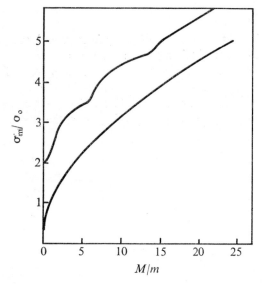

FIG. 2.21   Maximum stresses developed during impact loading. Upper curve, accurate solution; lower curve obtained by simply equating energies (after Timoshenko[16]).

i.e., for impacting masses less than about 10 times the mass of the rod.

This brief analysis, which of course refers only to Hookean materials, has been inserted here to emphasise the danger of using, as one's sole criterion of impact strength, the energy of impact necessary to cause fracture. It seems better to use the parameter $2v(E\rho)^{\frac{1}{2}}$, i.e., the value of σ_m as $(M/m) \rightarrow 0$ as the criterion. This has been pointed out previously by Haward [17] to whom reference should be made for further information.

(b) The second difficulty which arises in relating impact strength to strength under more controlled conditions of loading is that the stress-strain and fracture properties of polymers are rate-sensitive. The high rates of loading implicit in the term 'impact' thus have two superimposed effects; they give rise to transient stresses exceeding those expected under low loading rates, as discussed above, and secondly they actually alter the values of modulus, yield stress and fracture stress. These two factors together make it extremely difficult

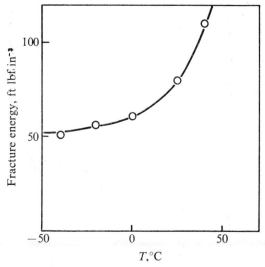

FIG. 2.22   Fracture energy of unplasticised PVC as a function of temperature (after Vincent[5]).

to predict the behaviour of a polymer under impact conditions from low-speed data and necessitate some form of high-speed test. Unfortunately many of the impact tests which have been devised and are in common use employ specimens having complex geometry, containing notches, etc., so that it becomes impossible to calculate the maximum stresses developed even in Hookean materials. In such cases it is useless to attempt to separate the effects of transient stresses from actual changes in material constants.

(c) In polymers the further complication of non-Hookean behaviour is almost invariably encountered so that even in the simplest geometrical situations it becomes difficult to predict maximum stresses. Not only are elastic stress waves propagated, but dispersion of the wave occurs because the elastic modulus is a function of strain. Slow moving plasticity waves may also be encountered.

To summarise, therefore, it is impossible in practice to separate the two basic effects of impact loading: the complex stress distribution

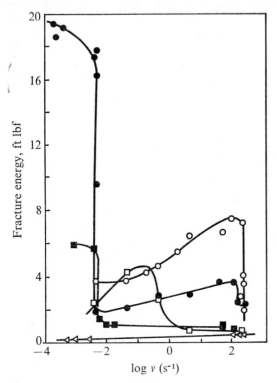

FIG. 2.23 Fracture energies of various polymers as functions of rate of strain (■) PMMA, (●) rigid PVC, (○,□) ethyl cellulose, (△) a phenolic resin (after Vincent[5]).

arising from travelling stress waves and giving rise to high maximum stresses, and the actual change in material properties under high rates of strain. It is therefore necessary to adopt some more empirical approach to the prediction and measurement of impact resistance. The usual method adopted is to measure the total energy expended in breaking some standard testpiece in two, the impulse being imparted by falling weights, a pendulum or a rotating flywheel. The relative merits of these various methods have been discussed by Vincent [18] but all suffer from the drawback that the 'impact strength' so defined is not a true material property but depends upon the shape and size of the testpiece.

Such tests are sufficient to answer the practical question whether or not a particular polymer is likely to fail in a brittle manner under

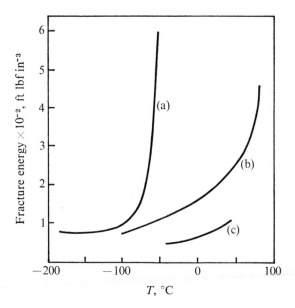

FIG. 2.24   Fracture energies in rigid PVC as functions of temperature (a) Flexural tests 18 in/min; (b) Tensile tests 4.10^{-3} to 0.5 min^{-1}; (c) Falling weight tensile impact tests (after Vincent[19]).

impact or be tough. The energy absorbed by a specimen before fracture is obviously related to its brittleness since this energy is simply the area under the load-deformation curve. A sudden fall in the fracture energy and thus in 'impact strength' is to be expected therefore as fracture passes from ductile to brittle and such a transition is often found when impact strength is measured as a function of temperature or speed of impact. The brittle-ductile fracture transitions observed under impact conditions are completely analogous to those discussed earlier for low rates of strain but the transition temperature will in general be higher at the high rates of strain encountered in impact tests and other complications may arise such as adiabatic heating of the specimen. Fig. 2.22 shows the decrease in impact strength for unplasticised PVC with reducing temperature and Fig. 2.23 that for PMMA, PVC, ethyl cellulose and a phenolic resin, with increasing rate of strain.[5]

The energy to fracture can, of course, be simply computed for a tensile fracture test at relatively low speeds and compared with that recorded in a tensile impact test. Such a comparison is shown in Fig. 2.24 for unplasticised PVC, in which the onset of yield and thus of ductile fracture appears to occur at a temperature some 120°C higher in the impact test.[19] This kind of behaviour opens the way to a possible prediction of impact behaviour from low-rate data by determining the brittle-ductile transition temperature range at a succession of rates of strain in tensile tests and extrapolating to the rate of strain obtained under impact. If the polymer concerned were known to obey the WLF equation up to the rates envisaged, the extrapolation could be accurate and the fracture energy, for example, precisely determined. The applicability of the WLF equation to the ultimate properties of non-rubbery polymers is severely limited, however, whilst the equation is known to fail for semi-crystalline materials. Even so it might be possible to make a reasonable empirical extrapolation.

References

1. VINCENT, P. I. *Br. J. appl. Phys.*, **13**, 578 (1962).
2. VINCENT, P. I. *Plastics, Lond.*, **26**, Nov. 141 (1961).
3. WARBURTON HALL, H., and HAZELL, E. A. *Techniques of Polymer Science* (S.C.I. Monograph No. 17), p. 226.
4. VINCENT, P. I. *Polymer*, **1**, 425 (1960).
5. VINCENT, P. I. *Plastics, Lond.*, **27**, Jan. 115 (1962).
6. ROETLING, J. A. *Polymer*, **6**, 615 (1965).
7. O'REILLY, J. M. *J. Polym. Sci.*, **57**, 429 (1962).
8. FLORY, P. J. *Ind. Eng. Chem.*, **38**, 429 (1946).
9. GREENSMITH, H. W., MULLINS, L., and THOMAS, A. G. *Chemistry and Physics of Rubberlike Substances*, p. 249, Maclaren and Sons Ltd. (1963).

10. TAYLOR, G. R., and DARIN, S. R. *J. Polym. Sci.*, **17**, 511 (1955).
11. SMITH, T. L. *J. Polym. Sci.*, **32**, 99 (1958).
12. SMITH, T. L. *Proc. R. Soc.*, *A*, **282**, 102 (1964).
13. TIMOSHENKO, S. *Strength of Materials*, Pt II, p. 444, D. Van Nostrand Co. Inc. (New York), 3rd ed. (1956).
14. VINCENT, P. I. *Plastics, Lond.*, **27**, Feb. 117 (1962).
15. GENT, A. N., and LINDLEY, P. B. *Proc. R. Soc.*, *A*, **249**, 195 (1959).
16. TIMOSHENKO, S. *Theory of Elasticity*, p. 389, McGraw-Hill (1934).
17. HAWARD, R. N. *Strength of Plastics and Glass*, Cleaver-Hume Press Ltd., London (1949).
18. VINCENT, P. I. *Plastics, Lond.*, **27**, Apr. 116, May 133, Jun. 136, Jul. 110 (1962).
19. VINCENT, P. I. *Plastics, Lond.*, **28**, Apr. 120 (1963).

CHAPTER 3

Fracture Phenomena
in Polymers II

3.1 CREEP FRACTURE

Creep fracture, or static fatigue, is the phenomenon of fracture under steady applied stresses lower than those required to cause fracture under direct-load conditions. As has been pointed out already there is no clear distinction between creep fracture and direct-load fracture since in the latter a finite time must always elapse between application of the stress and fracture, so that the dependence of fracture stress upon time (which is characteristic of creep fracture) is bound to be a factor in direct-load results also. Thus although in creep fracture we usually envisage the sudden application of a load which then remains constant for a time t until fracture occurs, it should be remembered that the variation in, say, tensile strength with rate of extension is probably caused by the same mechanism as operates to produce creep fracture.

This mode of failure may be characterised by a curve of stress against time to fracture, the latter quantity being usually plotted logarithmically. Fig. 3.1 shows a set of curves obtained for polyethylene under biaxial stress.[1] The time to fracture increases with decreasing load, the logarithmic plot being roughly linear in each of two regions, thus obeying an equation of the form

$$t = A \, e^{-B\sigma} \tag{3.1}$$

where A and B are constants which, of course, are different for each of the two regions of the curve. This form of equation is typical of creep fracture in a wide range of materials including glass. Temperature is another important variable and an increase in time to fracture is brought about by a fall in temperature; equation (3.1) becomes

$$t = C \, e^{-B\sigma} \, e^{U/kT} \tag{3.2}$$

where C and B are constants, U is the activation energy of the process and k is Boltzmann's constant. In Fig. 3.1, U has the value of about 7 kcal/mole.

The two distinct regions of the creep fracture curve illustrate a further interesting fact. To the left of the knee, i.e., at high stresses, the fracture strain was found to exceed 100 per cent and failure was ductile whilst to the right of the knee $\varepsilon_f < 10$ per cent and the fracture was brittle in nature. A brittle-ductile transition is thus evident in this mode of failure just as in direct-stress fracture. It was found that under

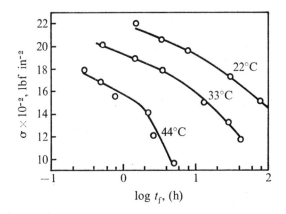

FIG. 3.1   Creep fracture in polyethylene under biaxial tension
(after Cooney[1]).

ductile conditions the polymer spherulites were deformed but that brittle fracture occurred by the coalescence of slowly growing fissures or cracks without significant overall deformation of the material.

These two essentially distinct types of creep fracture are observed in uniaxial tests also. Haward [2] studied the ductile creep fracture of cellulose acetate and cellulose nitrate and some of his data are given in Fig. 3.2 which shows the large creep strains which develop before fracture with increasing time. In these materials the creep strain is accompanied by a progressive whitening of the specimen indicating the creation of internal voids as the material stretches. Brittle creep fracture is found on the other hand, in polymers like polystyrene and PMMA. Data obtained by Regel [3] are given in Fig. 3.3 which shows first of all (curve a) the typical linear plot of log t against σ. As remarked earlier, brittle creep fracture in polymers is frequently accompanied by the formation and growth of a multitude of micro-cracks, this process being known as 'stress-crazing'. The apparent initiation time for the formation of such cracks (i.e., the time which elapses before cracks become visible at any given stress level) was also measured by Regel and is shown as curve b in Fig. 3.3. It is clear that the initiation time obeys the same equation as does the fracture time (equation (3.1)) with the same value of the constant B, but the constant A is about two orders of magnitude

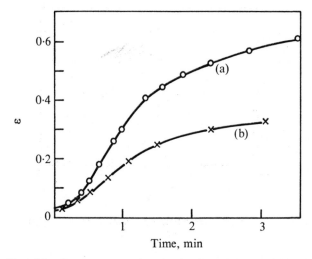

FIG. 3.2   Creep curves to fracture for (a) cellulose acetate at a nominal stress of 70·6 kgf cm^{-2}, (b) cellulose nitrate at a nominal stress of 305 kgf cm^{-2} (after Haward[2]).

greater for fracture than for initiation. It seems clear that stress-crazing is not only a concomitant of creep fracture but a true precursor and that the latter probably results eventually from the enlargement and joining up of the microfractures.

Stress-crazing has been widely studied and its main features well established. In the uniaxial tests the cracks grow perpendicular to the stress axis, though any internal (e.g., annealing) stresses may complicate the picture by modifying the principal stress directions in the body. It occurs at high stress levels in glassy polymers and is facilitated by increase in temperature and plasticisation, i.e., by any treatment calculated to increase molecular mobility. Maxwell and Rahm [4] used the intensity of light scattered from the craze cracks as a measure of the amount of crazing and Figs. 3.4 (*a*) and (*b*) show their results for the progress of cracking with time in polystyrene at various stress levels and over a range of temperatures. The density or population of microcracks increases with the stress level, a characteristic feature of

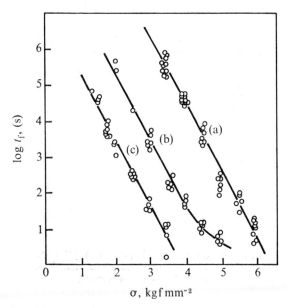

FIG. 3.3   Dependence upon stress of (a) time to fracture at 25°C, (b) apparent initiation time for microcracks at 25°C and (c) apparent initiation time for microcracks at 45°C. Data for PMMA (after Regel[3]).

all multiple-crack phenomena in polymers including environmental stress cracking. This effect can be attributed to the progressive 'activation' of surface flaws as the stress is raised and is illustrated by results of Regel [3] for PMMA (Fig. 3.5). The more closely spaced the microcracks become, of course, the shorter the distance they can propagate before mutual interference relieves the stress around any given crack and brings it to a halt. The vast majority of the cracks therefore do not develop to macroscopic proportions but at sufficiently high stresses a large number may coalesce to provide a locus for fracture through the body.

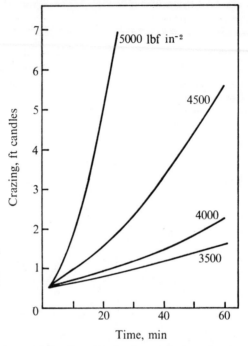

FIG. 3.4(a) Growth of microcracks in polystyrene
at 30°C measured by the intensity of scattered light
(after Maxwell and Rahm[4]).

3.2 CRACK PROPAGATION

Crack propagation differs from the other modes of rupture in that
it is a process fundamental to them all. There is a sense in which all
fracture phenomena represent the growth and spread of cracks,
fissures or tears under some particular set of conditions. In tensile
fracture the process occurs very rapidly, whilst in creep fracture it
may occur, initially, very slowly but in each case a crack or fissure is
originated and propagated to cause failure of the specimen. Fatigue
fracture, again, involves slow crack propagation but this time the
crack grows incrementally until the body fails. In so far as this
process is fundamental to all others it is inappropriate to discuss it at
great length in the present chapter. Most of the experimental work in
this field has been specifically designed to further our understanding
of fracture processes in general and there does not exist a large amount

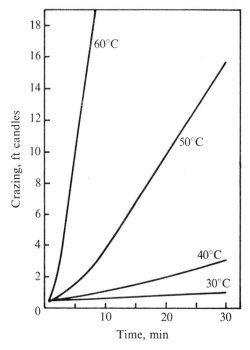

Fɪɢ. 3.4(*b*) Growth of microcracks in polystyrene
under a stress of 3500 lbf in⁻² measured by the
intensity of scattered light (after Maxwell and Rahm[4]).

of unconnected data as in the case of tensile fracture, for example.
An exception to this is the routine testing of tear resistance in
materials such as rubber in which a variety of arbitrary tests have
been applied which provide little basic information and often fail to
rank materials in the same order of 'tear resistance' as the test
method is varied. There are two aspects of crack propagation which
ought, however, to be mentioned here, namely 'notch sensitivity' and
high speed crack propagation.

(i) *Notch sensitivity*

It is a common observation that a tensile specimen breaks at lower
stress if it contains a sharp notch or, in the extreme, a crack. The
notch or crack concentrates stress at its tip and causes local failure
whilst the bulk of the specimen is still under comparatively low stress,

and this local failure causes a crack to propagate through the body. Thus a crack in a sheet of glass will 'run' under comparatively small applied forces and the material appears weak. Other materials however are less 'notch sensitive' in that the presence of a crack has relatively little influence upon their tensile strength, and such materials possess crack resistance either because plastic flow blunts the crack, as in ductile metals, or because of physical barriers to crack

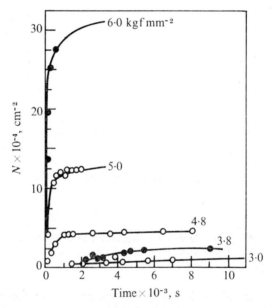

FIG. 3.5   Number of microcracks in unit surface area as a function of time and stress. PMMA+6% dibutyl-phthalate (after Regel[3]).

propagation such as the fibres in 'fibreglass' or other crack 'stopping' mechanisms that will be discussed in Chapter 5. One of the important tasks in the study of crack propagation is to achieve a satisfactory definition of crack resistance and then to correlate this resistance with the macroscopic properties and morphological features of the material in question. The presence of a crack may not only decrease the tensile strength of a body but under certain circumstances may cause brittle fracture in a material which under the same conditions would fail in a ductile manner if the crack were absent. This 'notch embrittlement' is best explained[5] by a diagram which shows the brittle fracture strength and yield stress of a polymer specimen as functions of temperature (Fig. 3.6). Suppose curve A to be the brittle fracture stress and curve B the yield stress of the bulk material. At the tip of the crack A will still apply but the yield stress will be higher

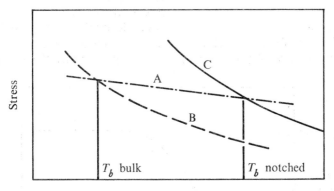

FIG. 3.6 Diagram illustrating origin of the phenomenon of notch brittleness. (A) brittle fracture stress, (B) yield stress of bulk, (C) yield stress at root of notch or crack.

(by a factor of up to three[6]) because of the triaxial stress system existing there. It must therefore be represented by a new curve C. The brittle-ductile transition temperature is thus elevated and if the temperature of test happens to lie between the two T_b values the phenomenon of notch brittleness will be observed.

(ii) *High speed fracture*

Although the most significant information on propagation is provided by experiments on controlled fracture, in which the velocity of propagation is kept low, a considerable amount of work has been done on catastrophic or high speed fracture. When fracture is not controlled, as in tensile failure for example, the velocity of fracture increases from a low initiation value to some maximum constant value V_m which often approximates to $0.5\ V_t$ where V_t is the velocity of propagation of transverse stress waves in the material. This is shown in Fig. 3.7 which gives data for glass [7] but behaviour in glassy plastics is qualitatively similar. Information of this nature is most readily obtained by irradiating the specimen during fracture with ultrasonic waves of known frequency, interaction between the waves and the fracture front causing periodic undulations in the fracture surface whose spacing immediately reveals the relative velocity of the fracture to the ultrasonic waves.[8] The maximum velocity of crack propagation has been variously predicted by theory to be 0·38 of the longitudinal stress wave velocity,[9] 0·5 of the transverse wave velocity,[10] and 0·6 of the transverse wave velocity,[11] the limiting factor in the last of these theories being a bifurcation of the crack tip at higher speeds of propagation. Experiment confirms the general

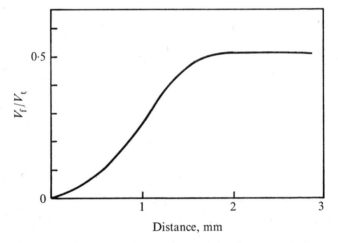

FIG. 3.7 Acceleration of a running crack in glass to a velocity approximately half that of the transverse wave (after Schardin[7]).

validity of these figures for a variety of materials [12] but the experimental scatter is such that it is impossible to say which of the above predictions is most nearly correct.

Polymeric materials do not give such reproducible results for maximum fracture velocities as the inorganic glasses. Steady 'maximum' velocities varying between 400 and 700 m s⁻¹ have been observed for example in PMMA.[12] The value is apparently related to the stress level in the specimen at the moment of fracture, an effect which is definitely not found in more brittle solids. A similar dependence of maximum fracture velocity upon stress level was found [13] in bursting tests on cellulose acetate film where the speed increased from 500 to 800 m s⁻¹ as the bursting tension was raised from 500 to 900 kgf cm^{-2}. A further observation is that several cracks may propagate simultaneously in a single polymer specimen at different yet stable velocities. It is very likely that the unusual behaviour of plastics results from the small amount of local plastic deformation that accompanies 'brittle' crack propagation in polymeric glasses (see Chapter 5) and which varies in amount according to the state and conditions of stress. In those polymers where plastic deformation at the crack tip is unlikely, as in cross-linked elastomers, the behaviour of high speed fracture appears to accord more closely with theory. Thus Mason [14] found a well defined limiting velocity 0·31 times the longitudinal wave velocity in gum SBR rubber at room temperature and Andrews [15] observed brittle fracture in filled natural rubber at liquid nitrogen temperatures in which a velocity 0·5 of the transverse wave velocity was attained.

3.3 FATIGUE FRACTURE

In contrast to the large amount of information available on the fatigue of metals, both from the phenomenological and theoretical viewpoints, the fatigue of polymeric solids has received very little attention. Exceptions to this are the fatigue of rubber, the fatigue of laminated plastics and a small amount of work on PMMA and on synthetic fibres.

A consideration of laminated plastics is beyond the scope of this book and a review of the subject has been given by Heywood.[16] It should be noted, however, that like metals these materials appear to possess a fatigue limit (i.e., a stress below which fracture by fatigue does not occur even after an infinite number of cycles), and give a fairly typical dependence of stress upon the logarithm of the number of cycles to fracture at stresses above this limit (Fig. 3.8). The existence of a fatigue limit has also been demonstrated for PMMA tested under a variety of conditions as shown by the results of Zarek [17] given in Table 3.1.

The value of the fatigue limit stress decreases with increasing frequency though this may be the result of rising local temperature caused by the hysteresial nature of the polymer and its low thermal conductivity. It has been reported that polycarbonate behaves similarly to PMMA in fatigue, a clear relationship between stress and the number of cycles to failure being obtained but other thermoplastics display wide scatter in the results. Polypropylene is exceptional in

7

that it proves almost impossible to fracture in conventional fatigue tests.

Several workers have considered the fatigue of synthetic fibres.[18] This subject is of obvious importance when the industrial applications of fibres are considered. During the fatigue process marked

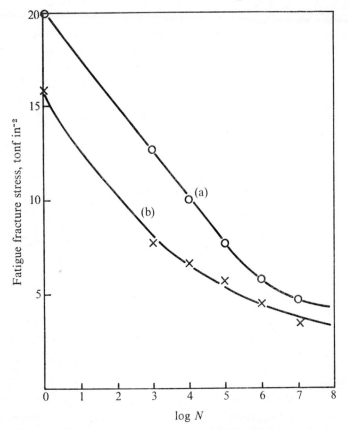

FIG. 3.8 Fatigue fracture curves for glass-fibre/plastic laminates. (a) polyester resin, (b) silicone resin[16].

changes occur in the fibre, notably elongation by creep and an increase in modulus illustrated for polyacrylic fibres in Fig. 3.9. The breaking strain is also diminished as cycling proceeds but perhaps the most significant finding is that the breaking stress of the majority of the fibre is not reduced by the fatigue process. Similar results are obtained for polyester and polyethylene fibres and indicate that fatigue fracture in these materials is localised both in space (i.e., it occurs at definite points in the fibre) and in time (i.e., it occurs rapidly over a short interval of time). Thus there is no overall degeneration of the fibre but rather a localized and rapid propagation of fatigue cracks to cause fracture during the final stages of cycling. Most of the time for fatigue appears to be absorbed in the generation of fissures of a size sufficient to cause significant changes in the strength of the fibre and thus sufficient to produce fracture. Prevorsek and Lyons [18] have presented a theory of fatigue crack

TABLE 3.1

Fatigue strengths of PMMA at various cycling frequencies

tonf in^{-2}

frequency min^{-1}	cycles to failure			
	10^4	10^5	10^6	10^7
95	2·4	2·0	1·9	1·9
190	2·0	1·6	1·5	1·5
950	1·6	1·2	1·2	1·2
1700	1·5	1·2	1·1	1·0
2250	1·5	1·1	0·9	0·9

nucleation which involves a statistical growth of small flaws similar to that discussed later in Chapter 4. The theory is successful in predicting a fatigue limit but unfortunately involves the assumption of values for several unknown parameters.

A full discussion of the fatigue of rubbers is held over until Chapter 5 since the theory of crack propagation developed there leads naturally to an explanation of the observed facts. In brief, however, it is found that fatigue fracture in elastomers involves only the incremental propagation of existing flaws of the order of 10^{-3} cm in size. No other process, such as flaw genesis, appears to be involved though because of the small size of the initial flaws and the fact that their growth rate increases with their size, there is an *apparent* induction period before visible fatigue cracks become evident. As in the case of other polymeric substances rubbers possess a fatigue stress limit below which fatigue cracks do not grow except as a consequence of ozone attack (see below). It is likely that ozone cracks constitute one source of the initial flaws from which fatigue cracks develop.

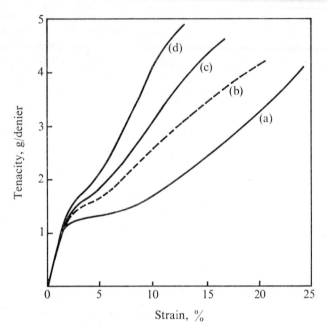

FIG. 3.9 Stress (or tenacity)-strain curves for polyacrylic fibres after subjection to various durations of fatigue. (a) 0 h, (b) 1·15 h, (c) 1·26 h, (d) 27-80 h (after Prevorsek and Lyons[18]).

3.4 CORROSION CRACKING

The cracking of solids placed under stress in a corrosive environment is a phenomenon of great practical importance and equal theoretical interest. It is variously referred to as stress corrosion cracking, environmental stress cracking and solvent crazing but we shall use only the first of these terms. It could be argued that the term 'corrosion' should only be used where chemical changes take place, as in metallic corrosion or ozone attack, but it can legitimately be employed to indicate any degenerative process involving interaction (whether physical or chemical) with the environment. Since the mechanics of the process are very similar in all cases considered it is convenient to use a single term to cover all these phenomena. The features of this mode of fracture are as follows:

(i) Cracks originate at the surface of the specimen and propagate invariably at right angles to the major principal stress direction.

(ii) The stress required to produce cracking is low compared with that needed to fracture the specimen under direct loading, and residual (annealing) stresses may be sufficient even in the absence of external loading.

(iii) A minimum stress usually exists below which no cracking will occur. This stress depends on the material and the environment.

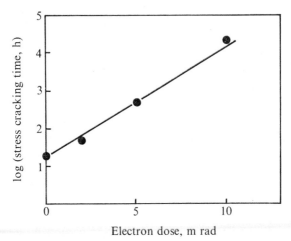

FIG. 3.10   Increase in stress corrosion resistance produced by irradiation cross-linking in polyethylene (after Haward and Mann[19]).

(iv) The time-to-fracture of a specimen subject to stress corrosion cracking is a function of the magnitude of the stress, the nature of the environment, the temperature and the molecular weight of the specimen.

Stress corrosion cracking in polymers occurs in environments as diverse as ozone gas, water and surface active liquids. Organic solvents are frequently found to cause stress cracking in plastics, especially amorphous ones; ozone is active towards unsaturated hydrocarbons, especially elastomers, and surface active media cause fracture in polyethylene. Each polymer-corrosive system is in one sense unique and has its own particular stress corrosion parameters and behaviour. Some interesting anomalies are found. For example, high density polyethylene is susceptible to stress corrosion cracking but polypropylene is, apparently, immune. On the other hand polyethylene itself becomes resistant if cross-linked, e.g., by irradiation or even when loaded with a particulate filler. Fig. 3.10 shows this

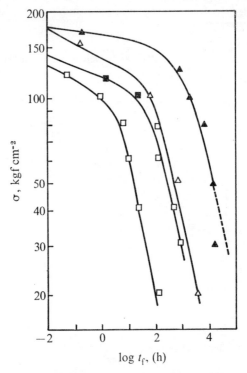

FIG. 3.11 Stress corrosion fracture in various high density polyethylenes in water (after Gaube[21]).

behaviour for polyethylene.[19] Molecular orientation can also impart resistance to cracking. Some systems that have been particularly studied are discussed below, but for more detailed information and literature references the reader is referred to a recent review.[20]

(i) Polyethylene in water and surface active liquids

The parameter usually employed to characterise corrosion stress cracking is the time-to-fracture of a standard strip of the material having a rectangular cross section and held under uniaxial tension.

Typical results for breaking time as a function of stress are given by Gaube [21] (Fig. 3.11) for some high density polyethylenes in water. Except at high stresses, where yield occurs in the specimen, the curve of log stress against log breaking time is a straight line with a slope of -2. An increase in temperature simply shifts this line to the left, i.e., to smaller breaking times, without changing its slope. Similar linear log-log plots have been obtained for polyethylene by other workers using a variety of stress cracking agents, particularly alcohols and surfactants like 'Igepal', but the slope of the curve varies from -2 to as much as -6 so that no very firm conclusions can be drawn. It is likely that the time-to-fracture is affected by a number of factors which are not under the control of the experimenter and that it is necessary to adopt a different approach to the characterisation of the process. The phenomenological aspects of corrosion cracking in polyethylene have been reviewed by Howard.[22]

(ii) *Rubber in an ozone-containing atmosphere*

Unsaturated hydrocarbon elastomers, such as natural rubber and styrene-butadiene rubber, suffer rapid cracking and eventual fracture if exposed to even small traces of ozone. The familiar phenomenon of 'perishing' is attributable to the small quantities of ozone present in the atmosphere. Only very low strains, of the order of 5 per cent, are required to cause cracking and the number of cracks increases with increasing strain above that level. Below the critical strain no cracking occurs even after prolonged exposure and no *apparent* reaction occurs between the ozone and the rubber. It has, however, been shown by electron microscopy that surface reaction does occur even at zero strain, but that the degraded layer of rubber thus produced protects the underlying material from further attack.

The resistance of rubbers to ozone cracking may be increased in various ways. Protective surface coatings may be used but are easily broken if the rubber is flexed. Alternatively chemical 'antiozonants' may be incorporated into the material which either increase the critical strain required to cause cracking or else slow down the rate of growth of cracks. It has been found, again by electron microscopy, that these protective chemicals act by modifying the surface inter-action between the rubber and the ozone making it more difficult for cracks to form and propagate.

It was shown by Braden and Gent [23] that the idea of a critical strain for ozone cracking was inadequate because this critical value was a function of the stiffness of the rubber and even of the surface finish. They showed that these difficulties were overcome by adopting a critical energy criterion and this is fully discussed in Chapter 5.

(iii) PMMA *in organic solvents*

Stress corrosion cracking occurs in polymethylmethacryalate when exposed to a range of organic solvents. Cracking is violent in those liquids which act as solvent for the polymer such as benzene or acetone, but also occurs in non-solvents like methylated spirit or petroleum ether. A critical stress is necessary to initiate cracking and just as in the case of ozone cracking in rubbers this may reflect a critical energy requirement. The critical stress appears to depend upon the solvent, and other parameters such as molecular weight, temperature and surface finish are also involved.[24]

(iv) *Craze matter*

Although it was at first believed that the cracks observed in stress corrosion cracking were simple fissures with only a single corrosive-polymer interface it is now known that this is not the case. In the ozone cracking of rubbers there is an intermediate layer of degraded rubber on the crack surfaces whilst in more rigid polymers the whole fissure is actually filled with a material, known as 'craze matter', which is neither pure polymer not pure corrosive but a mixture of the two. Spurr and Niegisch [25] have discussed the formation and propagation of corrosion stress cracks in terms of the conversion of polymer to craze matter by the combined action of local stress and solvent diffusion. It is a matter of common experience that even uniaxial stress on a body can facilitate diffusion through the material of which it is composed because of the hydrostatic tension associated with the stress system. Kambour [26] used an optical method (total internal reflection) to determine the refractive index of the craze matter in a variety of glassy polymers. He found that if the craze matter is considered to be composed of polymer and voids (everything other than polymer being regarded as 'void'), the void contents are as follows.

Polymer	Void content %
'Lexan' polycarbonate	45
PMMA	40
Polystyrene	40
Styrene-acrylonitrile co-polymer	60

Interestingly enough, it is found that the stress cracking or crazingly produced in plastics in the absence of a corrosive medium, and discussed earlier under the heading of creep fracture, is of a similar nature to that now considered. That is, the fissures produced in air also contain craze matter and the void content of this is identical to that obtained in the presence of a corrosive medium.

3.5 WEAR

Since polymers are not generally used in situations where they are exposed to heavy wear this subject has received little attention. An obvious exception is rubber which on account of its use in motor vehicle tyres has been widely studied in an attempt to understand and improve its resistance to abrasive wear. Other applications of polymers in which wear is of importance include the use of PTFE and nylon in low-friction bearing surfaces, the manufacture of flooring materials and the use of plastic gears. It is probable, therefore, that the process of wear or abrasion will increasingly become an object of interest and concern.

Polymeric solids have one important advantage over other materials in their ability to absorb mechanical energy visco-elastically. This kind of deformation, unlike plasticity, involves no permanent change in the material so that cumulative damage occurs less readily. Of course polymers also suffer non-visco-elastic deformations but it is a fact of experience that under conditions of wear by impact (a process typified by sand-blasting but also met in, e.g., the pumping of liquid suspensions) polymeric materials are frequently superior to metals. No one would expect a metal tyre to last as long as a rubber one, quite apart from considerations of traveller comfort! On the other hand polymers are in general far less resistant to sliding abrasion then metals because the high local temperatures developed at the sliding surfaces, which on a metal often produce protective oxide layers, lead to melting and thermal degradation of the molecules. This effect may be offset, however, by low coefficients of friction which, under mildly abrasive conditions, minimise the energy dissipated at the wearing surfaces.

The wear process in polymers is undoubtedly complex involving not only the mechanical removal of fragments from the surface but also partial melting and chemical reaction with the atmosphere. In the case of elastomers, however, it has been found possible to view the process primarily in terms of its mechanical aspects and to include

the other effects mentioned as super-imposed phenomena. It is not
our purpose here to review the considerable literature on the friction
and wear of rubber and the reader is referred elsewhere for such a
treatment of the subject.[27] It will suffice to say that the abrasive wear
of rubber, sliding on a wide variety of surfaces both coarse and
smooth, is found to occur by the removal of fine particles of the
rubber. Under many conditions an 'abrasion pattern' is set up (Fig.
3.12) which increases the rate of removal of material from the surface.[28]
This effect can be eliminated by frequent changes in the direction of
abrasion and the (lower) resultant wear has been denoted 'intrinsic
abrasion'. The removal of particles points clearly towards an
explanation of wear in terms of fracture, and recent experiments
designed to establish such a relationship will now be described.[29]

Blocks of various non-crystallising gum rubbers were abraded by
sliding on tracks of silicon carbide paper and measurements were
made over a range of velocities and temperatures, steps being taken
to avoid the formation of abrasion patterns. The parameters measured were the abraded volume per unit load and unit sliding distance
(the 'coefficient of abrasion' denoted A) and the coefficient of sliding
friction μ. The first finding of note was that the dependence of the
abrasion coefficient A upon the sliding velocity v obeys the WLF
transform. A master curve of A against $\log v$ is obtained by shifting
the curves obtained at different temperatures along the $\log v$ axis
by an amount $a(T)$. Master curves of this nature are shown in Fig.
3.13. The dependence of $a(T)$ upon T follows closely the form given
by the WLF equation. Since it has been previously shown [30] that the
coefficient of friction also obeys the transform, the quantity A/μ (the
'abradability') clearly does so too. The conclusion to be drawn from
these observations is that the wear process, like tensile fracture, is
visco-elastic in unfilled non-crystallising elastomers.

Even more information is forthcoming from the data relating wear
to temperature and some typical results are shown in Fig. 3.14 which
gives data on SBR, acrylonitrile-butadiene rubber (ABR), butyl
rubber and isomerised natural rubber (INR). At high temperatures
abrasion is severe but decreases with falling temperature to a minimum at around the onset of the rubber-to-glass transition region.
Below this temperature, as the material becomes rapidly harder, the
rate of wear rises abruptly. In order to test the suggestion that the
wear process arises from tensile fracture at the sliding surfaces, the
energy densities at fracture, W_f, in tensile tests were measured for

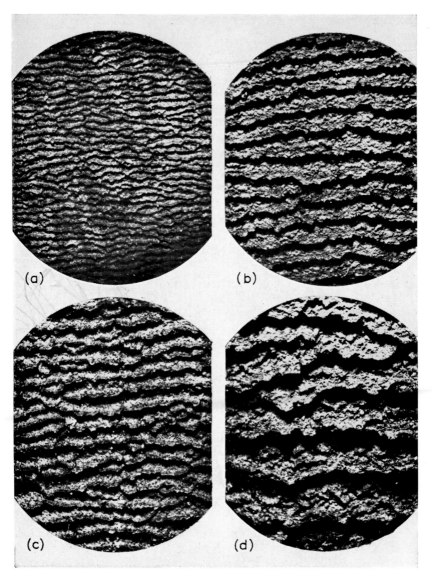

FIG. 3.12 Abrasion patterns on rubber surfaces. Magnification 15.
(a) NR+45pph HAF black, (b) NR+25 pph HAF black, on fine tarmac
track; (c) NR+45 pph HAF black, (d) NR+25 pph HAF black, on
coarse concrete track (after Schallamach[28]).

these same rubbers over the same temperature range. The rate of tensile straining was chosen as 100 sec^{-1} to correspond to the probable

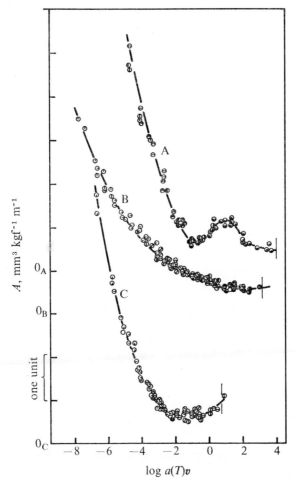

FIG. 3.13   WLF master curve for dependence of the abrasion coefficient upon rate of sliding and temperature (after Schallamach[29]).

rates of deformation at the surface at the particular sliding velocity used. The lower W_f, the higher ought the abrasive wear to be, so that in Fig. 3.14 the reciprocal of W_f has been plotted on a scale chosen to give the best fit between A/μ and W_f^{-1}. The close agreement between the two quantities encourages the belief that in these materials wear can be regarded essentially as a fracture process.

To this ought to be added the proviso that the track on which wear occurs may also influence the results. This is shown by the observation that addition of antioxidants to the rubber has little effect upon the results detailed above where a sharp abrasive was used but can greatly decrease the rate of wear when a smoother track is used. Oxidation processes are known to have little bearing on tensile

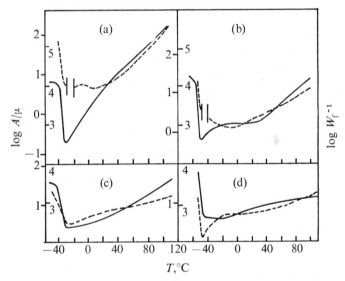

FIG. 3.14 Similarity between the abrasion coefficient (left-hand axis, dotted) and fracture energy (right-hand axis) as functions of temperature. (a) SBR, (b) ABR, (c) BR, (d) INR (after Schallamach[29]).

fracture but to greatly influence *fatigue* fracture and it seems justifiable to conclude that wear on smooth tracks, where the abrasive conditions are much less severe, takes place by fatigue rather than tensile failure. In both cases, however, the essentially mechanical nature of wear is predominant.

The foregoing discussion does not of course apply in detail to all kinds of rubber and certainly not to polymeric solids in general. The underlying principles should nevertheless be of great help in furthering our understanding of the wear process in polymers. A further point of value is that the results discussed in this section, which were obtained under carefully controlled conditions, can be related with a fair degree of success to the wear of actual components such as rolling tyres where the process is at first sight far more complex and the conditions largely uncontrolled.

3.6 FRACTURE AND THE MICROSTRUCTURE OF POLYMERS

(i) *General considerations*

In the theoretical discussion that ensues in the next two chapters the fracture behaviour of polymers is considered to be, in the main, determined by the macroscopic mechanical properties of the materials themselves. The effects of elasticity, plasticity and visco-elasticity upon fracture initiation and propagation will be discussed and a considerable understanding of fracture processes attained by this approach. It is clear, however, that the actual microstructure of the material cannot be ignored in any full discussion of our subject since fracture is essentially a microscopic process. By microstructure is meant the physical structure or texture of a material on a microscopic scale. It does not, strictly speaking, embrace crystal structure but it does include defect structure in crystals, grain or spherulite boundaries, phase separation, crystalline-amorphous texture and so on. The microstructure of a solid may influence its fracture behaviour in a variety of ways.

(*a*) It may give rise to inhomogeneous distribution of stress in the material. This inhomogeneity of stress may be harmful as in the case of cracks or other stress raisers or it may be beneficial as would be the case if strong continuous filamentous structures ran through the solid carrying most of the stress acting upon it. This latter situation exists in some biological polymers, in fibre-reinforced composite materials and probably in strong synthetic fibres. In the former case of stress raisers the microstructural features concerned cause premature initiation of fracture, as we shall see in our discussion of the flaw theory of strength (Chapter 4). In the latter case it is the propagation of fracture that is affected and generally inhibited (Chapter 5). The situation is far from simple however; a sufficiently dense distribution of stress raisers, like carbon black particles in a reinforced elastomer, can in fact impart strength by dissipating a great deal of energy during fracture propagation, whilst the fibres in a composite material may weaken the fatigue resistance by providing locations for fatigue crack generation.

(*b*) The microstructure may determine the path taken by fracture by providing loci of low breaking strength. Thus all inter-granular or interspherulitic fracture is caused by the weakness of the boundaries relative to the entities they separate. The fracture strength of a material will be much lower than would otherwise be expected if such routes exist for easy crack propagation. Boundaries may be intrinsically weak or alternatively provide easy access to corrosive media. In metals, for example the rate of diffusion of foreign atoms is far greater in the atomically disordered grain-boundaries than in the crystalline grains, and similar differences in penetration rate occur between the amorphous and crystalline regions of polymeric solids.

(*c*) Thirdly but by no means least important, the microstructure of the solid may determine or influence the macroscopic mechanical properties and thus affect fracture processes *indirectly*. In metals, for example, the plasticity which is exhibited by the bulk material and which plays a vital role in fracture is caused by the microstructural dislocations moving under the influence of the applied stress. It might be thought unnecessary to insist upon this point since it may be argued that the microstructure is having no effect other than that already allowed for by considering the bulk properties of the material. This is not, however, quite correct for the same microstructural features may give rise to rather different mechanical responses in the small region at the tip of a crack than in the bulk solid. This would occur, for example, in a metal if the multiplication of dislocations in the highly strained region surrounding a crack tip led to severe strain-hardening in this region which would then act differently in its subsequent response to stress than would the bulk material. Thus the elastic, plastic and visco-elastic properties of the small region subjected to fracture at the head of a growing crack may differ significantly from the corresponding properties of the bulk solid.

Considering the wealth of knowledge which exists concerning the interplay of microstructure and fracture in metals, a knowledge which is co-ordinated and rationalised in terms of the theory of dislocations, our understanding of the corresponding field in polymers is disappointing in the extreme. It must be remembered, however, that before the influence of microstructure upon fracture can be intelligently discussed, the nature of the microstructure must itself be known. It is here that progress has been so slow but the subject is fortunately now yielding to study and we can look forward to a rapid improvement in our knowledge of the physical structure of polymeric solids. The microstructure of polymers is one stage more complicated than that of metals in that a significant proportion of the material present is amorphous. In the extreme, of course, the fully amorphous polymer, whether glass or rubber, forms a particularly simple system whose microstructure consists only of such flaws as exist in an otherwise homogeneous solid. Most important polymers are, however, two phase systems containing both crystalline and amorphous regions organised in a wide variety of different ways and it is this that complicates the picture. Furthermore both crystalline and amorphous regions play a significant role in determining mechanical and fracture properties and a mechanism such as that of dislocation movement can only help us to understand events in one of these types of region, not both. In fact, although dislocations have been observed in polymer crystals [31] it is not yet certain that they have any bearing upon the deformation of bulk polymeric solids. In the absence of any comprehensive knowledge of polymer microstructure and bereft of a basic theory such as that of dislocations to describe non-elastic deformation in these materials we can only here indicate what empirical knowledge has so far accumulated on the subject of fracture and microstructure.

(ii) *Two-phase or reinforced materials*

The fracture strength of polymers may be greatly improved by the incorporation of a second solid phase. Very often the second phase is actually mixed into the parent material mechanically as in the case of carbon loaded rubber whilst in other materials such as some high impact-strength polymers, it is precipitated by polymerisation *in situ*. Such two-phase materials are said to be 'reinforced' by the additional phase and are also referred to as composite materials. Apart from the extreme importance of reinforcement in industrial applications these materials provide particularly simple systems in which to study the general problem of the effects of microstructure upon mechanical properties. A glass-fibre reinforced plastic, for example, is a simpler system than a synthetic fibre (in which a similar structure may exist by virtue of its crystalline-amorphous texture), because we can vary the quantity of glass fibre, its orientation, its fibre-length and so on in an attempt to understand the properties of such a material. The three most common types of reinforced polymers are the fibre-reinforced composites, like 'fibreglass', pigment-reinforced polymers (e.g., rubber filled with carbon black) and the high impact-strength plastics in which a brittle parent material is modified by a fine dispersion of rubbery particles.

(a) Fibre reinforced composites generally consist of glass fibres in a matrix of an amorphous, thermosetting resin, although recently

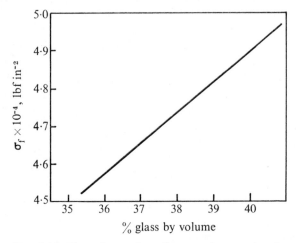

FIG. 3.15   Dependence of tensile strength upon the glass content of a polymer/glass-fabric laminate (after Haward, Ch. 2 reference 17).

ceramic 'whiskers' and carbon fibres with very high modulus and strength have been incorporated into resins. The purpose of the fibre component is to impart high modulus, resistance to brittle cracking and enhanced creep resistance to the polymer. Contrariwise the polymer protects the fibres from surface damage which drastically reduces their strength in normal use. In many commercial materials the glass fibres are present in the form of a woven fabric which is then laminated with, for example, an allyl resin. A consideration of such materials lies beyond the scope of this book and reference should be made elsewhere for further information on laminates.[16] However the dependence of tensile strength upon the amount of glass incorporated in such a material provides an indication of the effectiveness of reinforcement and is shown in Fig. 3.15. Fibre-reinforced composites possess higher elastic moduli than the parent polymer by virtue of the presence of stiffening fibres and theoretical predictions have been made for the composite modulus as a function of the amount and orientation of fibre component as well as the moduli of the component materials.[32] The enhancement of tensile strength together with the increase in modulus is generally such that the energy for fracture is higher then either of the component materials—a fact of obvious practical importance in applications requiring good impact strength.

The mechanism of fracture in a fibre-reinforced composite has been the subject of theoretical study.[33] The transfer of tensile stress between the matrix and a filament embedded in it is such that the stress in the filament rises linearly from a zero value at its ends (this ignores end-effects) reaching a maximum half-way along the fibre. The longer the fibre, the higher the stress it carries and the more likely it is to fracture. As a composite material is subjected to increasing tensile stress, therefore, the longer fibres fracture first and the overall effect is a progressive reduction in mean fibre length. When the fibres are so short that they carry only a small portion of the load the matrix material will fail often by plastic flow, and the specimen will fracture. The theory is substantiated, at least qualitatively, by model experiments. In practice the fracture process in such a material is complicated by stress concentrations at fibre ends and by breakdown or plastic flow at the fibre-resin interface. The latter is of particular significance in the fatigue fracture of composites since fatigue cracks can be initiated at the interface. Alternatively fatigue cracks in the resin may be halted by fibres and *vice versa* but the balance of these effects is such that the fatigue resistance of composite materials is not generally of a high order.

(*b*) The reinforcement of polymers by the incorporation of fine particulate materials ('pigments') has been chiefly exploited in the field of rubbers, where some striking effects are observed. The tensile strength of non-crystallising rubbers can be increased by orders of magnitude by the addition of 30 per cent by volume of carbon black, so that a material having the consistency of cheese becomes useable in a motor-car tyre with a life of ten to twenty thousand miles. Of equal interest is the fact that a crystallising rubber, like natural rubber, which already has a high tensile strength receives no further resistance to fracture if carbon black is added, though in both kinds of elastomers the elastic modulus and mechanical hysteresis are both greatly increased. The inclusion of carbon black has relatively little effect on the fatigue resistance of rubbers.

Fig. 3.16 shows the fracture surface of a non-crystallising rubber (styrene-butadiene co-polymer) as revealed by replica electron microscopy. The carbon black particles are seen either in silhouette, where they have been removed from the rupture surface by the replica, or else as bumps in that surface. The quantity of particles removed (the 'extracted filler') varies according to the type of carbon black and the conditions of fracture, but the fact that *any* are removed indicates that the particles have been separated from the rubber matrix under the high stresses developed during the passage of rupture. A replica removes no particles from a moulded surface. Breakdown between the matrix and the particles (among other things) causes energy dissipation around the fracture path and thus makes the material stronger than before. In a crystallising rubber there is already a large energy dissipation due to the mechanical hysteresis associated with crystallisation under strain and subsequent re-melting so that the carbon black particles do not materially alter the energy required to propagate fracture. This reinforcement mechanism will be discussed more fully in Chapter 5, but it is worth noting here the paradox that breakdown between particles and matrix, which strengthens the material, arises because the particle-matrix boundary (being subject to concentrations of stress) is a point of weakness in the solid. A sufficient number of dispersed points of weakness thus provide an effective means of reinforcement.

(c) *High-impact plastics.* Although it has been noted that fibre-reinforced materials have improved impact strength the description 'high-impact' is generally reserved for brittle plastics which have been rendered resilient or tough by the addition of a dispersed rubber phase. These materials may be produced by direct blending of polymer latices or by co-polymerisation as in the case of an ABS (acrylonitrile, butadiene, styrene) co-polymer. The ultimate properties of the material are critically dependent on the method of preparation, the best results being obtained with a fine, uniform dispersion of the rubberlike phase. The impact strength of some high-impact polystyrenes is given in Fig. 3.17 as a function of the rubbery content, the diagram also showing the yield strength of the materials.[19] The impact resistance rises by a factor of almost 10 as the rubber content is increased from zero to 8 per cent, but it will be noticed that this improvement is accounted for by a corresponding decrease in the

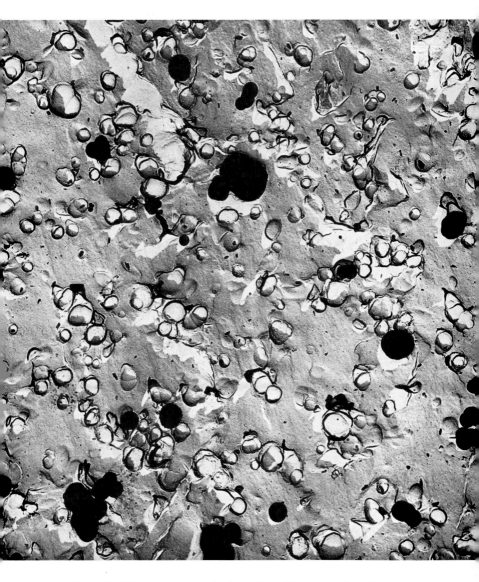

FIG. 3.16 Electron micrograph of a replicated fracture surface of carbon filled rubber. Magnification 12 000.

yield strength. That is, by reducing the yield stress below the brittle fracture stress of the material plastic flow is permitted to occur before fracture and the fracture energy is thus greatly enhanced.

The reinforcing particles have been supposed to act as crack-stoppers but it is equally likely that the stress concentrations at the

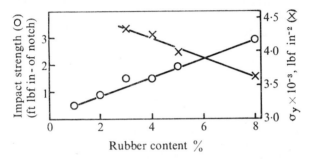

FIG. 3.17   Impact strength and yield stress of high impact poly-styrenes as functions of the rubber content (after Haward and Mann[19]).

surfaces of embedded particles give rise to local plastic deformation which absorbs energy and makes crack propagation more difficult. Such local deformation has, in fact, been observed in fracture surfaces [19] viewed in the electron microscope and if this is the process chiefly responsible for inhibiting crack propagation it is completely analogous to that occurring in carbon-filled rubbers.

(iii) *Crystalline-amorphous texture of polymers*

In contrast to structures artificially introduced into polymeric materials we now turn to the intrinsic microstructure of rubbers and plastics which comes into being as the material is solidified from the melt or as a result of annealing, working, stretching or chemical reactions. It is a common observation that the strength of polymeric materials rises with increasing crystallinity. Fig. 3.18 shows that the tensile strength of natural rubber which crystallises on extension is consistently higher than that of a whole range of amorphous rubbers when plotted against reduced temperature. Fig. 3.19 shows the tensile yield stresses of a range of polyethylene as a function of density; high density, of course, corresponding to high crystallinity.[19] The reason for this dependence is not at all obvious, though some suggestions can be advanced. Firstly the crystalline regions may simply act as cross-links preventing the molecules from slipping relative to one another and it is significant in this context that chemical cross-linking by irradiation also greatly increases the tensile strength of polyethylene.[33] Under these conditions it becomes necessary either to break molecules to produce yield or incipient fracture, or else to allow that yield can occur in the *crystalline* regions to permit the specimen as a whole to change its shape. In either case the resistance of the material to deformation and fracture will be enhanced. The

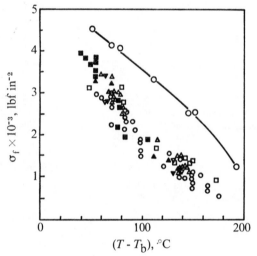

FIG. 3.18. Tensile strength of various rubbers plotted against a reduced temperature scale. Solid line shows data for natural rubber; lower points are data from seven different non-crystallising rubbers (after Greensmith, Mullins and Thomas, Chap. 2 reference 9).

more detailed considerations of Chapter 5 show that the energy required for fracture, and consequently the tensile strength of a material, may increase with the yield stress and the major contribution of crystallinity to tensile strength may be in this realm.

If the amorphous regions of the polymer are in a glassy condition a second result of crystallinity may be to impart ductility to a material which would otherwise be brittle. Such an effect would be critically dependent upon the ductility of the crystalline regions themselves and this emphasises the importance of the mechanical properties of single polymer crystals (see below). Ductility in crystalline polymers is a complex phenomenon being dependent upon molecular orientation as well as upon the absolute proportion of crystalline material, and it is possible that the orientation exerts its influence via modifications to the crystalline texture as discussed presently.

(a) *Fracture of polymer single crystals.* As was discussed in Chapter 1 many polymers in bulk are known to consist of platelike crystals

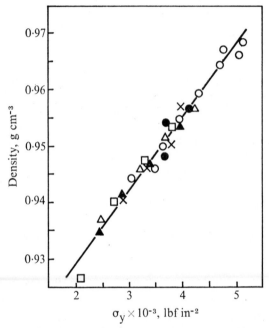

FIG. 3.19   Dependence of yield stress upon density in polyethylene (after Haward and Mann[19]).

stacked together but interspersed by amorphous regions. One rather indirect but nevertheless important approach is therefore to study the fracture behaviour of single platelet crystals, such as can be grown from dilute solutions of the polymer, with a view to evaluating the contribution of the crystalline phase to macroscopic fracture. Investigations of this kind have been carried out by depositing polyethylene single crystals on extensible substrates and stretching them under observation in the electron microscope.[34] Cracks have been obtained in the single crystal platelets at strains as low as 10 per cent and are crystallographically oriented, lying in those (100),

(010) and (110) planes which happen to be nearly perpendicular to the draw direction. On the other hand plastic deformations of up to 100 per cent have been obtained, the crystal concerned displaying deformation bands resembling slip bands in a metal. Diffraction studies indicate that this plastic deformation occurs through a combination of twinning, crystal transformation (e.g., orthorhombic to monoclinic in polyethylene) and slip. A third effect frequently found in strained single crystals is a combination of brittle cracking and plastic flow. Cracks are observed which are, however, spanned by filaments of drawn material, the quantity of drawn polymer being small if the cracks lie along the previously mentioned crystallographic planes the first two of which are also the growth faces of the crystal. Most of the work on the fracture and deformation of single crystals has so far been done using polyethylene but broadly similar results are obtained in nylon and polyoxymethylene, and there is reason to suppose that the deformation mechanisms observed in isolated single crystals are similar in kind to those obtained in bulk polymers. It is, of course, a big step from the single crystal to the bulk and the picture is not yet very complete but these studies do serve to indicate that the crystalline phase is potentially involved in the origin and propagation of fracture. It has sometimes been erroneously supposed that the 'crystallites' in a semi-crystalline polymer act merely as filler particles and that fracture occurs only through the amorphous regions.

(b) *Fracture of spherulites.* Coming next to the fracture of bulk semi-crystalline polymers we find a certain amount of information on the fracture of spherulitic materials. This subject has been studied by Keith and Padden [35] who examined thin cast films of polyethylene under the optical microscope. Spherulites grown by slow cooling from the melt fractured in a brittle manner at low stresses, the fracture following an irregular path bearing no relationship to spherulite boundaries or other obvious structural features. In more rapidly crystallised films brittle cracking was observed at spherulite boundaries whilst at still higher rates of cooling drawing occurred at the boundaries prior to fracture. In the most rapidly cooled films the spherulites themselves deform plastically either with or without drawing at the boundaries.

Cracking and drawing at inter-spherulite boundaries is to be expected in terms of the denudation of these regions during the crystallisation process. If the crystallising solid cannot contract

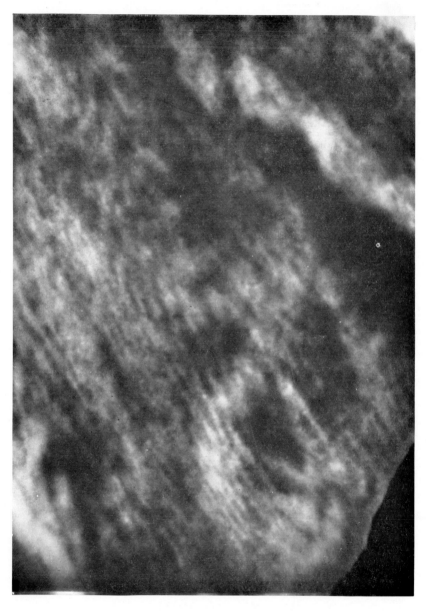

FIG. 3.20   Electron micrograph of an ultra-thin section of polyethylene
showing deformed spherulite. Magnification 7000.

freely (as it certainly cannot once growing spherulites begin to impinge upon one another) the increase in density occasioned by crystallisation must be accompanied by a decrease in density of the remnant amorphous regions which include the inter-spherulite boundaries. At high cooling rates it might be expected that these compensating density changes will be accommodated within the spherulite rather than at the boundaries, so that the latter will not suffer the weakening typical of more slowly cooled materials.

The wholesale drawing or plastic deformation of spherulites is typical of bulk polymers at ambient temperatures and the brittle cracking sometimes found in cast films is usually absent. A drawn polymer possesses a fibrous texture and splits readily along the direction of extension. In spite of this apparently different micro-structure the original spherulitic structure is not necessarily destroyed and highly elongated spherulites and other remnant features may be seen in the drawn material. Such a spherulite is shown in Fig. 3.20 which is an electron micrograph of a microtome section of low density polyethylene drawn to an extension ratio of about four.

Brittle fracture can of course be induced at low temperatures and the fracture surfaces so obtained have been studied using replica methods. Except in rare cases (e.g., fractionated linear polyethylene) fully brittle, inter-lamellar fracture is not observed and the surfaces reveal evidence of local plastic deformation where the fracture crosses lamellar regions. As in metallic brittle fracture therefore there is reason to believe that small amounts of plastic deformation occur even at liquid nitrogen temperatures and it is possible that local yielding is responsible for the initiation of macroscopically brittle fracture as in the case of metals.

(c) *Tensile strength of crystallised elastomers.* A new approach to the influence of crystalline microstructure upon fracture properties has become possible following the observation that polymers crystal-lised under strain possess crystalline morphologies which are a function of the strain. Elastomers like natural rubber are most suitable for this kind of investigation since they can be readily held under permanent strain during crystallisation, though in principle any suitable polymer can be cross-linked and raised above its crystal melting point to bring it into an elastomeric condition. The variation of morphology with strain for natural rubber has already been discussed in Chapter 1; as strain is increased the spherulitic texture characteristic of an unstrained polymer gives way to a filamentous texture perpendicular to the strain axis, the filaments increasing in number until at high strains only filament nuclei have space to develop, the nuclei forming chains *along* the strain axis and giving rise to a fibrous texture in that direction.

In some recent experiments Andrews and Reed [36] have studied the variations in tensile properties which accompany these morphological

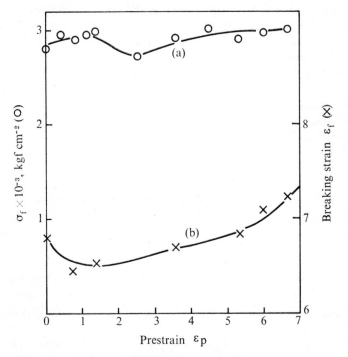

FIG. 3.21   Variation of (a) fracture stress and (b) fracture strain with the prestrain at which crystallisation occurred. Natural rubber crystallised and tested at −26°C.

changes. Specimens of natural rubber were held at various pre-strains ranging from zero to 800 per cent and crystallised at −26°C. The specimens were then mounted, in a stress-free condition, in a testing machine and their tensile strengths and elongations to fracture determined, the temperature being maintained below −20°C to avoid melting of the crystalline regions. Some results are given in Fig. 3.21(*a*) and (*b*) which show respectively the ultimate tensile strength (referred to the cross section at fracture and thus a true measure of material strength) and the elongation at fracture (referred to the original length, i.e., before pre-extension was applied). All points are the mean of six tests. The full significance of these curves is not yet clear but the decrease in the tensile strength at pre-extensions of about 150 per cent appears to correspond to the development of the perpendicular filamentous structure, a texture which might be intuitively branded as weak.

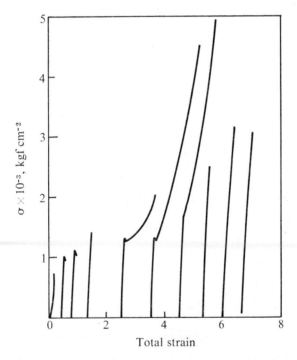

FIG. 3.22   Stress-strain curves of natural rubber specimens crystallised at −26°C at various prestrains and tested at −120°C.

At −20°C the amorphous regions in natural rubber will be rubbery and not glassy since the glass transition temperature is about −80°C. Specimens tested below −80°C after crystallisation at −26°C exhibit brittleness for zero pre-extension (spherulitic morphology) but yield and ductility above 200 per cent pre-extension (Fig. 3.22).

It seems clear therefore that some morphological systems or textures are more likely to exhibit yield than are others even when they contain similar quantities of the crystalline phase, and since brittleness is usually related to low strength the influence of texture upon the latter is again underlined. The actual increase in fracture stress at −120°C with pre-extension is shown in Fig. 3.23 both for material

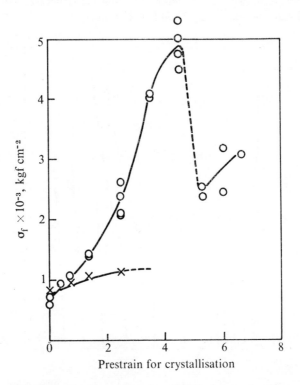

FIG. 3.23 Fracture stress at −120°C of natural rubber crystallised at −26°C and at various prestrains (circles). The crosses represent data on oriented but uncrystallised specimens.

crystallised at −26°C and for specimens oriented but not crystallised. The rise in strength due to molecular orientation alone is small but when crystallinity is present also, the rise is considerable and far greater than any effect observed in the same specimens tested at −26°C. It can therefore be said that the *condition* of the amorphous regions exerts a strong influence upon fracture properties even when the crystalline texture or morphological organisation remains unchanged.

References

1. COONEY, J. L. *J. appl. Polym. Sci.*, **8**, 1889 (1964).
2. HAWARD, R. N. *Trans. Faraday Soc.*, **38**, 394 (1942).
3. REGAL, V. R. *Soviet Phys.-Tech. Phys.*, **1**, 353 (1956).
4. MAXWELL, B., and RAHM, L. F. *Ind. Eng. Chem.*, **41**, 1988 (1949).
5. LUDWIK, P. *Elemente der Technologischen Mechanik*, Springer, Berlin (1909).
6. OROWAN, E., *et al. Strength and Testing of Materials*, Vol. 1, H.M. Stationary Office, London (1952).
7. SCHARDIN, H. *Fracture* (ed. B. L. Averbach), p. 304, John Wiley and Sons, Inc. (1959).
8. KERKHOF, F. *Naturwissenschaften*, **40**, 478 (1953).
9. ROBERTS, D. K., and WELLS, A. A. *Engineering*, **178**, 820 (1954).
10. PONCELET, E. F. *Metals Technol.*, **11** Technical Publication 1684 (April 1944).
11. YOFFE, E. H. *Phil. Mag.*, **42**, 739 (1951).
12. SCHARDIN, H. *Fracture* (ed. B. L. Averbach), p. 324, John Wiley and Sons, Inc. (1959).
13. REICHENBACH, H. *Actes du 2ème Congrès Int. Phot. Cinem. Ultra-Rapides*, p. 333, Paris (1954).
14. MASON, P. *J. appl. Phys.*, 1146 (1958).
15. ANDREWS, E. H. *J. appl. Phys.*, **30**, 740 (1959).
16. HEYWOOD, R. B. *R.A.E. Tech. Note Chem.* 1337 (1958). British Plastics Federation Reinforced Plastics Tech. Conf. (1958).
17. ZAREK, J. M. *Br. Plast.*, **30**, 399 (1957).
18. PREVORSEK, D., and LYONS, W. J. *J. appl. Phys.*, **35**, 3152 (1964).
19. HAWARD, R. N., and MANN, J. *Proc. R. Soc.*, *A*, **282**, 120 (1964).
20. ROSEN, B. (Ed). *Fracture Processes in Polymeric Solids*, p. 276, John Wiley and Sons, Inc. (1964).
21. GAUBE, E. *Kunstoffe*, **49**, 446 (1959).
22. HOWARD, J. B. *S.P.E. Jl.*, **15**, 397 (1959).
23. BRADEN, M., and GENT, A. N. *J. appl. Polym. Sci.*, **3**, 90 (1960).
24. WOLOCK, I., *et al.* National Advisory Ctte for Aeronautics, Res. Memo. 54A04 (1954).
25. SPURR, O. K., and NIEGISCH, W. D. *J. appl. Polym. Sci.*, **6**, 585 (1962).
26. KAMBOUR, R. P. *J. Polym. Sci.*, *A*, **2**, 4159 (1964).
27. SCHALLAMACH, A. *Chemistry and Physics of Rubberlike Substances* (ed. L. Bateman), p. 355, Maclaren and Sons Ltd. (1963).

28. SCHALLAMACH, A. *Wear*, **1**, 384 (1958).
29. SCHALLAMACH, A. *Proceedings NRPRA Jubilee Conf., Cambridge* 1964 (ed. L. Mullins), Maclaren (1965).
30. GROSCH, K. A. *Proc. R. Soc., A*, **274**, 21 (1963).
31. HOLLAND, V. F. *J. appl. Phys.*, **35**, 3235 (1964).
32. COX, H. L. *Br. J. appl. Phys.*, **3**, 72 (1952).
33. KELLY, A. *Proc. R. Soc., A*, **282**, (1964).
34. GEIL, P. H. *Polymer Single Crystals*, p. 441, Interscience Publishers (1963).
35. KEITH, H. D., and PADDEN, F. J. *J. Polym. Sci.*, **41**, 525 (1959).
36. ANDREWS, E. H., and REED, P. E. To be published.

CHAPTER 4

Initiation of Fracture

The discussion of fracture phenomena in the foregoing chapters raises one fundamental question. Must these different phenomena be conceived as different processes, independent of one another and incapable of a common interpretation, or is a unified approach to fracture possible? The answer, fortunately, is that much can be done by a unified theory of fracture to explain the bewildering array of information available on fracture processes in solids. The ideal is to explain each apparently distinct phenomenon as a particular case of a general fracture mechanism, feeding into the general theory the specific factors of, for example, mode of fracture, material microstructure and environmental conditions which apply in that case. The realisation of such an ideal is still beyond our grasp but it is possible at least to set out in the right direction and this is the intention of the next two chapters.

It was stated earlier that there were processes common to all fracture phenomena and these may be reduced to two, namely initiation and propagation. Initiation may be defined as the act of creating a flaw or crack in the material capable of propagating under the applied stresses, and propagation as the subsequent growth of that flaw or crack up to the moment of macroscopic fracture. It is convenient to regard initiation and propagation as distinct processes, as for example when we distinguish 'initiation-controlled' fracture phenomena from 'propagation-controlled' ones, but it is not intended that they should be regarded as unconnected. They are rather different aspects of the same overall process, that of fracture, and it is not always easy in practice to separate the two.

This chapter is concerned with the initiation of fracture and with the explanation of such fracture phenomena as can be understood in terms of initiation. The following chapter will consider the role of propagation in determining the macroscopic failure properties of polymers.

4.1 THEORETICAL AND ACTUAL STRENGTHS

If the stress throughout a loaded body remained perfectly uniform, and if the material itself were completely homogeneous down to the atomic level, all atomic bonds in the direction of strain would be equally stressed and all would fail at the identical moment. The result would be complete dissociation of the atoms comprising the body much as a liquid passes into the vapour state at the critical temperature. Considering this to occur under a uniaxial stress one can arrive

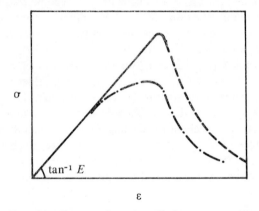

FIG. 4.1 Interatomic stress-displacement curves (schematic). Upper curve assumes linearity, lower curve shows a more realistic behaviour.

at an estimate of the ideal tensile strength of the material since most laws of interatomic force indicate a maximum in the force-displacement curve when the interatomic bond has been strained by less than 20 per cent. Assuming a linear relation between stress and strain up to this point, the slope of the line, of course, being the Young's Modulus E of the material (see Fig. 4.1) we obtain a maximum fracture strength,

$$\sigma_f = 0{\cdot}2E. \tag{4.1}$$

A more realistic assumption about the shape of the interatomic force-displacement curve (Fig. 4.1) reduces this estimate to

$$\sigma_f = \alpha E \tag{4.2}$$

where $\alpha \sim 0.1$. A similar calculation can be carried out to decide the theoretical shear strength of a material and one obtains

$$\tau_f = \alpha G \qquad (4.3)$$

where again $\alpha \sim 0.1$ and G is the shear modulus. Refinements [1] in the assumed force-deflection curve reduce the predicted value of τ_f further giving $\alpha \sim 0.03$.

The discrepancy between these theoretical estimates and the actual strength of materials is apparent when one realises that glass breaks under direct tensile stresses of $10^{-3} E$ and that common metals and alloys yield plastically at $\alpha \sim 10^{-3}$ and break by plastic strain concentration at $\alpha \sim 10^{-2}$. Steels may have yield strengths as high as $10^{-2} G$.

These relatively low strengths are typical of bulk material which cannot be expected to fulfil the conditions of homogeneity laid down earlier. In specially prepared materials, often fibres or crystalline whiskers, much higher strengths are regularly obtained, strengths which in some cases attain the theoretical value. Cottrell [2] has given a list of some such 'special' materials with their tensile strengths, the appropriate value for α and for comparison, the tensile strengths of comparable bulk materials. Some of his figures are reproduced below.

TABLE 4.1

Some observed tensile strengths (10^2 kgf cm^{-2})

Special materials	σ_f	α	Bulk materials	σ_f
Graphite whisker	2400	0·024	Nylon	50
* Al$_2$O$_3$ whisker	1500	0·028	Hard Al alloy	50
Fe whisker	1300	0·044⎱	Cast iron	28
Drawn high-C steel	420	0·02 ⎰		
Cu whisker	350	0·03	Drawn Cu wire	55
Glass fibre	360	0·035	Glass	10
* Asbestos fibre	150	0·008	Hard wood	10

(* Note that in these cases there is no strict comparison between the special and the bulk materials, the atomic bonding being of a different kind.)

A difference in fracture behaviour is noticeable between many of the high strength materials and their bulk counterparts for the former often disintegrate at the moment of fracture whereas the bulk material generally breaks into two or at most several large fragments. This is particularly true of high strength glass fibres and it may be that something like the theoretical behaviour is being obtained in these cases. There remains, however, a discrepancy between the highest observed strengths and ideal behaviour, a factor of about 2 or 3 in α. Whilst this latter discrepancy may be attributable to faulty theory the much larger divergence found in the case of bulk solids is clearly real and must arise from lack of homogeneity, i.e., from the presence of stress-raising flaws, dislocations or similar features in the material.

Calculations of theoretical strength have been made for polymers using not only the general principles employed above (which predict tensile strengths from 10^3–10^4 kgf cm^{-2}) but also from a knowledge of the specific properties of the chemical bonds present in polymeric solids. Mark [3] has summarised the results of calculations based on oriented cellulose and finds,

(a) If the primary valence bonds are broken simultaneously across the whole section of the specimen a tensile strength of 150 000 kgf cm^{-2} would be expected.

(b) If the chains lay with all their ends in a plane perpendicular to the tensile axis and rupture occurred only of Van der Waals' bonds, the tensile strength should be 2700 kgf cm^{-2}.

(c) If the molecules contain 400 glucose units and if the fracture occurs by the chains slipping over each other the tensile strength should be 9000 kgf cm^{-2}.

Actual values of tensile strength for oriented polymers at room temperature are in the region of 5000 kgf cm^{-2} suggesting superficially that Mark's third mechanism is the one operating in the fracture of such materials. Bulk thermoplastics, however, break mostly at around 100 kgf cm^{-2} and thermosetting resins, in which co-valent bonds must be ruptured, have tensile strengths as low as 400 kgf cm^{-2} compared with theoretical values a thousand times greater.

As has been mentioned in Chapter 2, reduction in the temperatures causes an increase in the brittle fracture strength of thermoplastics, as does increase in the rate of straining, and values as high as 15 000 kgf cm^{-2} have been observed [4] for tensile strength at $-180°C$. Although this figure is still low compared with Mark's estimate for co-valent bond breakage it compares favourably with predictions made from the elastic modulus ($E = 4$ to 12×10^4 kgf cm^{-2}). The discrepancy between the two calculations arises simply because the elastic moduli found in practice are, even in oriented polymers at low temperature, smaller by a factor of ten than the theoretical moduli and, as Vincent [4] has pointed out, one cannot expect to reach the theoretical strength until one has attained the theoretical modulus.

To summarise the data for polymeric materials therefore we find that if full orientation of the molecules could be realised, so that each chain were actively load-bearing, values of tensile strength should be obtained approaching the theoretical value for co-valent bond breakage, provided the test is carried out at very low temperature. Disorientation of the molecules and increasing temperature both lead to a rapid fall in the tensile strength and account for the low values normally observed. The reason for this decrease, as well as for the small residual discrepancy with theory even at low temperatures, must now be discussed.

4.2 FLAW THEORY OF FRACTURE

(i) *Initiation of fracture from pre-existent flaws*

The discrepancy between predicted and actual strengths can be explained in terms of stress-raising flaws which give rise to local stresses greatly in excess of those nominally borne by the body under test. These flaws may be physical discontinuities such as cracks or surface scratches, discontinuities of elastic moduli (as when a particle of one material is embedded in a matrix of a second) or irregularities in the ordering of atoms such as dislocations in a crystal lattice. The magnitude of the stress concentration varies according to the geometry of the flaw, but factors of 1000 may easily be produced between the local and nominal stresses. Flaws may give rise to fracture (or in the case of dislocations, to yield) by propagation through the body and without such propagation no macroscopic effect would be observed. The propagation phase of fracture, however, will be discussed later and it is assumed for the moment that once a flaw begins to propagate under the influence of the applied forces it will continue to do so, i.e., it will propagate catastrophically. The simple flaw theory, therefore, states that fracture occurs when flaws become capable of propagation. It is this act of 'becoming' that we have called initiation and on the theory outlined below initiation is a sufficient and necessary condition for macroscopic

9

fracture. As will be seen, this theory is useful to explain brittle fracture phenomena but requires considerable modification before it can be generally applied.

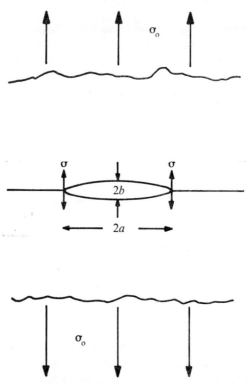

FIG. 4.2 Elliptical hole in a uniformly loaded infinite plate.

That flaws, in the form of surface scratches or craze cracks, drastically reduce the tensile strength of brittle solids has been amply demonstrated.[5] The removal of the surface layer of a glass rod by chemical etching can increase the tensile strength by a factor of five hundred, whilst the intentional introduction of a deep scratch is equally effective in lowering the strength of the same material.

Consider a flaw in the form of an elliptical crack with semi-axes a and b in an infinite sheet of material under uniaxial stress σ_0 applied perpendicular to the length of the crack (Fig. 4.2). By use of classical elasticity theory, Inglis [6] showed that a maximum tensile component of stress σ occurs at the end of the elliptical crack of magnitude,

$$\sigma = \sigma_0(1+2a/b). \tag{4.4}$$

The term enclosed in brackets equals σ/σ_0 and is the stress-concentration factor. Clearly for long, narrow cracks $(a \gg b)$ this factor can become extremely large. Equation (4.4) can be put into another useful form by substituting $\rho = b^2/a$ where ρ is the radius of curvature of the sharp end of the crack, giving

$$\sigma = \sigma_0(1+2(a/\rho)^{\frac{1}{2}}) \tag{4.5}$$

or if $a \gg \rho$

$$\sigma = \sigma_0 2(a/\rho)^{\frac{1}{2}}. \tag{4.6}$$

If now we set the applied stress σ_0 equal to that required to cause fracture at the crack tip, it follows that σ must be σ_m the theoretical breaking stress of the material and we thus obtain for the tensile strength

$$\sigma_f = \frac{\sigma_m}{2}\left(\frac{\rho}{a}\right)^{\frac{1}{2}} \tag{4.7}$$

This equation is interesting but of little practical use since it involves the experimentally inaccessible quantity ρ. In the cleavage fracture of a crystalline solid ρ must be of the order of the interatomic spacing and is therefore fairly precisely known, but in many materials, especially polymers, it is a much larger and rather indeterminate quantity.

The difficulty may be overcome, however, by considering not only the forces acting at the crack tip but the work expended there in elongating the crack. For simplicity consider again the cleavage of a single crystal and assume that the force-distance curve of Fig. 4.1 is linear. The work done in separating two atoms on opposite sides of the cleavage plane will be of the order of

$$\tfrac{1}{2}\sigma_m d^2 \times \varepsilon_m d \tag{4.8}$$

where ε_m is the maximum strain of the bond and d is the interatomic spacing. The work per unit area of cleavage plane will be simply

$$\frac{d\sigma_m \varepsilon_m}{2} = \frac{\sigma_m^2 d}{2E}.$$

But, by definition, this is the surface energy, $2S$, of the (two) freshly created interfaces, so that

$$2S = \frac{\sigma_m^2 d}{2E.}$$

Substituting for σ_m from equation (4.7) this becomes,

$$S = \frac{4\sigma_f^2 a}{4E} \cdot \frac{d}{\rho}$$

or,

$$\sigma_f = \left(\frac{ES}{a} \cdot \frac{\rho}{d}\right)^{\frac{1}{2}}. \tag{4.9}$$

Providing $\rho \sim d$ as it must be for cleavage fracture, we obtain finally

$$\sigma_f \sim \left(\frac{ES}{a}\right)^{\frac{1}{2}}. \tag{4.10}$$

This equation, which gives the fracture stress to be expected of a body containing cracks of length $2a$ in terms of the ascertainable quantities E and S, is of fundamental importance. Apart from numerical factors it is identical to an equation derived by Griffith [7] from consideration of the elastic stored energy lost from a strained lamina by the introduction of an Inglis-type elliptical crack. Griffith found this energy to be

$$\frac{\pi \sigma_0^2 a^2}{E} \tag{4.11}$$

per unit thickness of the lamina and postulated that a crack of length $2a$ would propagate if the increase in this quantity per unit growth of the crack were greater than the surface energy required by the newly created interfaces, i.e., if

$$\frac{\partial}{\partial a}\left\{-\frac{\pi \sigma_0^2 a^2}{E} + 4aS\right\} > 0 \tag{4.12}$$

and at fracture

$$\sigma_0 = \sigma_f = \left(\frac{2ES}{\pi a}\right)^{\frac{1}{2}}. \tag{4.13}$$

This equation assumes plane stress conditions. In plane strain the equation becomes

$$\sigma_f = \left(\frac{2ES}{\pi(1-\mu^2)a}\right)^{\frac{1}{2}} \tag{4.14}$$

where μ is Poisson's ratio.

The essential identity between equations (4.13) and (4.10) is apparent though at first rather surprising. Why should an argument that involves the arrangement and spacing of atoms and the radius of a crack tip yield the same answer as one which invokes only macroscopic considerations? The answer is, of course, that the microscopic aspects are implicit in Griffith's treatment, concealed in the concept of surface energy the definition and explanation of which both appeal to the atomistic nature of matter. The more important thing to grasp, however, is that the energy-balance approach of Griffith and the idea of a critical stress criterion for fracture (i.e., the stress at the crack tip attaining σ_m the theoretical fracture stress as used to derive equation (4.10)) are substantially equivalent. Before

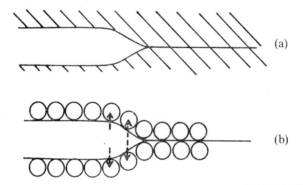

(a)

(b)

FIG. 4.3   Cleavage crack according to (a) continuum view and (b) atomistic view.

leaving this point reference ought, perhaps, to be made to a difficulty which many have in visualising the critical stress criterion for a cleavage crack. The difficulty arises because such a crack must have the form sketched in Fig. 4.3(a), that is, it must have a *negative* tip radius because of its cusp-like shape. Clearly a negative value for ρ in equation (4.9) would give an imaginary fracture stress! The error in this argument lies in its assumption that the material can be regarded as a continuum on the atomic level. In fact, of course, there is no continuum; we must consider the forces between atoms and when this is done the problem is immediately resolved. Whereas the continuum model predicts infinite stress at the tip when ρ becomes zero, it is clear that the stress there has a maximum value given by the binding forces of the atoms, which though in the process of being forced apart continue to attract one another across the geometrical 'gap' between them (see Fig. 4.3(b)). The 'negative tip radius' of continuum theory is thus non-existent when we consider the thing that really matters, namely the *continuity of the stress field*. This solution of the continuum difficulty was first advanced by Elliott, who also used the critical stress criterion applied to the atomic model of Fig. 4.3(b) to derive fracture criteria essentially similar in form to that of Griffith, again emphasising the equivalence of critical stress and energy balance approaches.

A few important conclusions may be derived from equation (4.13). Firstly, in a given uniform stress field, a crack which has reached the critical length to satisfy the equation must always continue to satisfy it as it grows. Increase in a can only decrease the stress necessary to propagate the crack so that the latter must continue to grow. In fact, of course, it will not only grow but also accelerate since the elastic energy released by growth increasingly exceeds that required in the form of surface energy. This substantiates the earlier statement that in simple flaw theory attainment of the critical condition is a sufficient criterion for macroscopic fracture.

Secondly fracture stress should be proportional to $E^{\frac{1}{2}}$ and this is in contradistinction to the behaviour expected of ideal strength (Chapter 4.1) where σ_f should be proportional to E. Thirdly any changes in surface energy, due for example to the presence of a contaminating absorbed layer of moisture, will affect the values recorded for tensile strength.

(ii) *Griffith theory applied to multiaxial stress systems*

The Griffith theory has been extended to the case of two and three dimensional stress systems.[8,9] It is in fact found that stresses normal to the lamina containing the crack have little influence upon the fracture criterion. Considering the stresses in the plane of the lamina, namely σ_x acting along the crack axis and σ_y perpendicular to it, the conditions for instability are found to be

$$\sigma_y^2 - \alpha\sigma_x\sigma_y = 16GS/\pi a \tag{4.15}$$

where $\alpha = (1-4\mu)$ for plane strain and $(1-3\mu)/(1+\mu)$ for plane strain,[10] and G is the shear modulus.

A more general treatment considers principal stresses σ_1 and σ_2 acting so that σ_2 makes an angle of θ with the crack axis.[11] (θ is taken as less than 45°, larger angles being covered by interchanging σ_1 and σ_2.) Two cases are found.

(a) When $3\sigma_1 + \sigma_2 > 0$

In this case a crack for which θ is zero, i.e., a crack perpendicular to the line of action of σ_1, will always propagate before cracks oriented differently. The critical value of σ_1 at which it does so is independent of the magnitude of σ_2 and is denoted σ_c.

(b) When $3\sigma_1 + \sigma_2 < 0$

Under these conditions the first crack to propagate is that for which

$$\cos 2\theta = -\tfrac{1}{2}\frac{\sigma_1 - \sigma_2}{\sigma_1 + \sigma_2} \qquad (4.16)$$

and the critical condition is given by

$$(\sigma_1 - \sigma_2)^2 + 8\sigma_c(\sigma_1 + \sigma_2) = 0. \qquad (4.17)$$

These equations are useful in envisaging what should happen in a bi-axially stressed material containing a randomly oriented array of cracks. One particular result may be noticed. If the specimen is subject to a uniaxial compressive stress $-\sigma_2(\sigma_1 = 0)$ a crack having $\theta = 30°$ should propagate preferentially and at a value $\sigma_2 = 8\sigma_c$, i.e., at a stress eight times the critical uniaxial tensile stress for fracture.

(iii) *Tests of the flaw theory*

There is no doubt that the equations given above provide a good qualitative account of the effect of flaws upon the strength of brittle materials. The theory also has some quantitative success and the dependence of fracture strength upon crack dimensions is particularly well authenticated for a variety of materials. Fig. 4.4 shows the results of model experiments carried out by Berry [12] on PMMA and polystyrene in which cracks of known lengths were introduced into test specimens whose apparent tensile strengths were then measured. The fracture strength of the specimens falls off with increasing crack length according to the relation

$$\sigma_f = Ka^{-\frac{1}{2}} \qquad (4.18)$$

as predicted by the flaw theory and the values obtained for the fitting constant K give, from equation (4.13) the surface energy S (the Young's Modulus being known).

$$\begin{array}{lll}
\text{Polystyrene} & S = 1\cdot7 \times 10^6 \text{ erg cm}^{-2} \\
\text{PMMA} & S = 3 \times 10^5 \;\; \text{erg cm}^{-2}.
\end{array}$$

It is at once evident that these values for 'surface energy' are far in excess of any possible true figure since even close-packed atomic arrangements give surface energies not exceeding 10^3 erg cm^{-2}. Berry's results show, therefore, that the flaw theory correctly predicts the effect of crack depth but is an inadequate account of the fracture process in brittle plastics.

A further point of considerable interest arises from Fig. 4.4. At sufficiently low sizes of the artificial flaw the experimental points for polystyrene deviate from the relation $\sigma_f \propto a^{-\frac{1}{2}}$ so that the tensile strength of specimens with no artificial flaw is much lower than

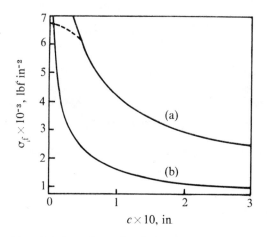

FIG. 4.4 Experimental relation between fracture stress and crack depth in (a) polystyrene and (b) PMMA (after Berry[12]).

would be expected and lower than that for PMMA although polystyrene is stronger at larger flaw sizes (i.e., it has a higher S value). This behaviour is explained by the presence of natural flaws in the material which take control of fracture when the artificial flaw becomes smaller than those already present. The precise size of the natural or inherent flaw can of course be estimated from equation (4.13) using the tensile strength of the un-cracked material and the value of S derived from Fig. 4.4. For polystyrene the flaw size is about 1 mm and for PMMA only 0·05 mm which explains the higher natural strength of the latter material in spite of its lower S value.

An attempt to apply the Griffith equation to elastomers containing artificial flaws is less successful. Bueche and Berry [13] found that neither the relation $\sigma_f \propto a^{-\frac{1}{2}}$ nor $\sigma_f \propto E^{\frac{1}{2}}$ were confirmed. This failure is not unexpected considering that the Griffith theory is based upon classical elasticity which is not obeyed by highly extensible materials. This difficulty is overcome for elastomers by a theory developed by Rivlin and Thomas [14] (see below).

4.3 GENERALISATION OF THE FLAW THEORY

There are four respects in which the flaw theory presented so far is inadequate. Firstly the physical basis of the theory is clearly suspect because of the impossible values found for surface energy. Secondly the theory is strictly inapplicable to most real materials because it assumes Hookean behaviour, perfect elasticity and infinitesimal strain. This, of course, is the simple consequence of using classical elasticity theory in its derivation. Thirdly there is the logical dilemma that Griffith cracks cannot in fact exist in an unstrained body since the energy balance of equation (4.12) demands that a crack must close up completely in the absence of externally applied stresses! Fourthly, the theory is unable to account for time-dependent fracture phenomena such as creep fracture. In spite of these objections, however, there is every reason to believe that the flaw theory is basically sound and our task must therefore be to modify it in such a way as to meet them.

(i) *Taking account of non-elastic deformation at the crack tip*

The first step in the generalisation of Griffith's theory was taken by Orowan [15] who found that metals, like plastics gave unreasonably high values for the quantity S in the simple theory and inferred that the energy required to propagate the crack consisted of two parts. The first is the surface energy already taken into account and the second is the energy absorbed at the crack tip prior to fracture in local plastic deformation. In many materials there is visual evidence that such irreversible deformation does take place and having some idea of the width of the plastically deformed region a crude calculation soon shows that the quantity of energy so absorbed is likely to greatly exceed the surface energy. Providing plastic flow is limited to the vicinity of the crack, so that the specimen as a whole remains elastic, the theory can be very simply modified by replacing S by a quantity $\mathscr{T}$ the 'characteristic energy' for crack propagation, where $\mathscr{T}$ includes both S and the energy dissipated in plastic flow. It also includes any other energy dissipation such as visco-elastic energy losses which may or may not result in permanent local deformations. All these energies, of course, must be referred to unit area of crack interface since the dimensions of $\mathscr{T}$ are the same as those of S, namely energy per unit area. The replacement of S by $\mathscr{T}$ immediately reconciles the theory with results such as those of Berry. It does however introduce difficulties of its own as we shall see later. In particular, although the value of $\mathscr{T}$ can still be regarded as characteristic of the material, its dependence on such variables as rate of testing, temperature and conditions of stress at the crack tip is far greater than that of surface energy.

(ii) *Materials not obeying classical elasticity theory*

Rivlin and Thomas [14] have proposed a theory which, whilst completely analogous to the modified Griffith theory, avoids any appeal to classical elasticity theory. Like Griffith they consider the balance of energy between the strained body and the crack and propose as a criterion for propagation the inequality

$$-\frac{\partial \mathscr{E}}{\partial A}\bigg|_{1} \geqslant \mathscr{T} \qquad (4.19)$$

where $\mathscr{T}$ is again a characteristic energy (per unit area), $\mathscr{E}$ is the elastically stored energy in the specimen as a whole and A is the interfacial area of the crack. The suffix 1 denotes that no external work is done upon the system during interchange of energy between the body as a whole and the crack. So far the criterion is perfectly general.

If particular cases are now considered it is possible to evaluate the left-hand side of the equation in terms of easily measurable quantities like force, strain and so on. Two examples are given below, the specimen in each case consisting of a sheet of uniform thickness h containing a crack of length c (c is now used in place of $2a$ to avoid repetition of the factor 2) so that $A = 2ch$ and equation (4.19) becomes

$$-\frac{1}{2h}\frac{\partial \mathscr{E}}{\partial c}\bigg|_{1} \geqslant \mathscr{T} \qquad (4.20)$$

The first case is that of a parallel-sided strip of material loaded in tension and containing a short edge crack running only a short distance into the specimen (Fig. 4.5). A similar specimen containing no crack possesses a uniform strain-energy density (i.e., strain-energy per volume) of, say W. The insertion of the crack reduces this energy to zero over the shaded area of the sheet, an area that general considerations suggest will be proportional to c^2 because of its

FIG. 4.5 Sheet specimen with edge crack.

triangular shape. The loss of energy caused by introducing the crack is therefore

$$Kc^2hW \tag{4.21}$$

where K is a constant or at least a slowly varying number and it is assumed that introduction of the crack has only a second-order effect upon the value of W at points remote from the crack. The change in this energy loss if the crack propagates Δc is given, in the limit, by

$$-\frac{\partial \mathscr{E}}{\partial c}\bigg|_1 = 2KchW$$

For fracture to occur, the right-hand side of this equation must equal $2h\mathscr{T}$ and this will happen at some critical value W_c of the stored energy density in the bulk of the test piece given by

$$W_c = \mathscr{T}/Kc \tag{4.22}$$

Reference back to equation (4.13) shows the close similarity between Griffith's result and the present one, for squaring and dividing by $2E$ gives

$$\frac{\sigma_f^2}{2E} = \frac{S}{\pi a} \qquad (4.23)$$

the left-hand side of which is, of course, the energy density in the bulk of the specimen. Griffith's equation is simply a special case, applicable to materials obeying classical elasticity theory, of Rivlin and Thomas's more general theory. The quantity W in equation (4.21) is generally easy to determine even in non-Hookean materials provided the crack length is small compared with the specimen width. The

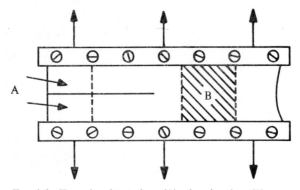

FIG. 4.6   'Pure shear' test piece. (A) relaxed region, (B) pure shear region.

quantity K can be evaluated for classically elastic materials by a proper analysis of the stress distribution and for other materials experimentally, by studying the load-extension curves of specimens containing cracks of different lengths and calculating the work done on the specimens as a whole in separating the grips by a given distance. Its classical value is π and experimentally it is found to lie between 1 and 3 for an extensible material like rubber.[16]

A second case is that of a sheet of material as shown in Fig. 4.6 gripped along its edges and containing a long crack parallel to those edges. Providing the specimen is long compared with the distance between the grips the shaded area will be in a state of pure shear, the strains in the plane of the sheet being $\varepsilon_x = 0$ and ε_z, and perpendicular to it $\varepsilon_y = -\varepsilon_z$. Regions of the specimen near the crack tip and at the uncracked end of the sheet will be in an undetermined state of stress but regions at the other end of the specimen, where the latter is divided by the crack, will be stress free. The effect, therefore, of propagation of the crack will be to remove a portion Δc in length from the pure-shear region and transfer it to the unstrained state. The loss of energy is thus expressible as

$$-\Delta \mathscr{E} = Wlh\Delta c$$

where W is now the stored-energy density in the material in pure shear and l is the distance between the grips before application of strain. This gives

$$-\frac{1}{2h}\frac{\partial \mathscr{E}}{\partial c}\bigg|_1 = \tfrac{1}{2} Wl. \qquad (4.24)$$

To apply this case practically W must be determined in terms of ε_z the strain in pure shear, either from the known elastic properties of the material or else empirically.

These two examples reveal the power of the Rivlin and Thomas approach and for further instances reference should be made to the literature.[17] Up to the present time this approach has proved highly successful in treating materials, like rubber, which violate classical elasticity in being non-Hookean and having finite extensibility. It should be noted, however, that application should also be possible where non-elastic deformations occur in the bulk of the specimen and this has, in fact, been done in the case of visco-elastic liquids.[18] It is only necessary to realise that in these cases $\partial \mathscr{E}/\partial A$ must refer to the elastically recoverable component of stored energy and not to the total energy expended upon the system.

(iii) *Stable existence of Griffith cracks*

As was remarked earlier the pure energy-balance hypothesis of Griffith would necessitate the closure of cracks in unstrained bodies since $\partial \mathscr{E}/\partial A$ would be zero and free energy would be minimised by elimination of the crack interface. This difficulty was originally countered by supposing that the cracks (which, Griffith proposed, exist continually in all materials) were stabilised by impurities, foreign bodies or contaminant surface layers. It is now possible to suggest plastic deformation at the crack tip as a further, and more convincing, reason for their failure to close up. Even a highly brittle material like glass is subject to plastic flow in the minute region surrounding a crack tip so that once established, there is every reason for a crack to be maintained.

This is not, however, the whole story. It is necessary to ask how the cracks come into being in the first instance without causing any catastrophic failure of the material in the process. It is difficult to imagine them arising from prior stressing such as occurs during, say, cooling from the melt without the production of visible damage. It is easier to accept that they arise from atmospheric corrosion at the surface in conjunction, perhaps, with residual stresses in the surface layer, and surface crazing is observed in glass (when suitably treated) and some brittle plastics. Even so it is difficult to believe that intrinsic flaws such as those proposed by Berry for polystyrene of the order of 1 mm deep can pre-exist without detection. In the latter case at least it is necessary to consider the production or genesis of the flaws during the actual course of the fracture test. This process can be seen to occur during the tensile testing of some brittle plastics when before fracture the surface is found to contain very many growing cracks only a few of which are involved in the final fracture of the specimen. At the point of macrosopic fracture the growing flaws must have achieved some size which effectively serves as the 'intrinsic' flaw size, i.e., the cracks act at that moment to all intents and purposes as if they had been present in the material from the beginning. As noticed previously this effective flaw size c_0 can be calculated from equation (4.13) which re-arranged becomes,

$$\frac{c_0}{2} = \frac{2ES}{\pi\sigma_f^2} \tag{4.25}$$

using values for S obtained from crack propagation data (strictly, of course, S should here be replaced by $\mathcal{T}$). Alternatively the fracture stress σ_f' of a specimen with a preformed crack c_0' can be measured and then

$$c_0\sigma_f^2 = c_0'\sigma_f'^2$$
$$c_0 = c_0'\left(\frac{\sigma_f'}{\sigma_f}\right)^2. \tag{4.26}$$

Using such methods, Berry [19] has investigated the variation of the intrinsic flaw size c_0 in PMMA with a range of parameters. Fig. 4.7 shows c_0 as a function of temperature where it is seen to vary from about 0·5 to 2×10^{-2} cm having a minimum value at $-20°$C. The intrinsic flaw size is influenced by molecular orientation, increasing to about 1 mm for a sheet stretched biaxially by 65 per cent, and also increases by a factor of rather less than two as the molecular weight of the PMMA varies from 98 000 to 6 000 000. The inherent flaw size in polystyrene at room temperature is about 1 mm, as mentioned earlier in section 4.2.

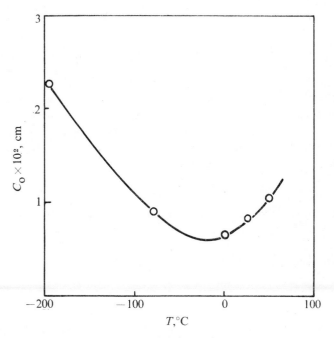

FIG. 4.7   Intrinsic flaw size in PMMA as a function of temperature (after Berry[19]).

4.4 Time Dependent Fracture

The inability of simple flaw theory to explain creep-fracture or any time-dependence of fracture processes has been met in two ways. According to one view,[20] surface flaws develop to the critical Griffith size by a process of stress-corrosion (see Chapter 3) the corrosive medium in the case of glass being atmospheric water vapour. A surface flaw, though too small to propagate according to the energy-balance condition, nevertheless possesses at its tip a concentration of stress giving rise to dilatation and the more rapid penetration of corrosive molecules. These weaken the material and the flaw grows at a rate governed by the rate of diffusion of the corrosive medium, a rate which in turn depends upon the local stress and the temperature. This view is supported by observations on glass that time-dependence of fracture is eliminated by testing in a vacuum. A quantitative expression for the time-to-fracture t_f under a given stress σ_f has been derived from this theory having the form

$$\log t_f = A + B \log \sigma_f \qquad (4.27)$$

where A and B are constants, and this agrees well with experiment.

It is difficult to see, however, how this theory can apply to materials in general since many polymers especially are not affected chemically by atmospheric constituents. An alternative idea [21] is that flaws may grow to the critical Griffith size by a statistical-mechanical process in which the rate of growth is governed by the balance between two opposed, thermally-activated processes affecting chemical bonds:

(i)   bond intact→bond broken,

(ii)   bond broken→bond remade,

In the unstrained state the probabilities of (i) and (ii) are equal but if stress is applied the probability of process (i) is increased by a reduction in its activation energy whilst the probability of (ii) is diminished. The rate of crack advance is then proportional to the rate R of bond breakage at the tip and this is

$$R \simeq K \exp\left\{-(U - f(\sigma))/kT\right\} \qquad (4.28)$$

where K is a constant, U is the activation energy in the unstressed state and $f(\sigma)$ a function of the applied stress. Taking the time-to-fracture as inversely proportional to R we obtain

$$\log t_f = K_1 + (U - f(\sigma_f))/kT$$
$$= K_1 + f_1(\sigma_f)/kT \qquad (4.29)$$

where K_1 is another constant and f_1 another function. This equation is very similar to that obtained from the stress-corrosion theory and although experiments confirm the logarithmic dependence on time they fail to differentiate between the different theories.

The two theories, however, have in common the concept that flaws smaller than the critical size of the simple theory are capable of growth under the influence of stress until they attain that size. There are thus two phases in the fracture process, a slow, stress and temperature-dependent phase taking place isothermally, and a catastrophic adiabatic phase resulting in macroscopic fracture. The first phase almost certainly corresponds to the mirror zone observed in fracture surfaces around the fracture origin in glassy materials (see Chapter 6) so that the critical Griffith flaw size can be directly measured. It is found that the mirror zone radius increases as the magnitude of σ_f decreases in accordance with the theory.

4.5 Fracture in Polymers as an Initiation-Controlled Phenomenon

The modified flaw-theory outlined in the present chapter provides us with an explanation of some of the qualitative aspects of fracture in polymers. The relative weakness of bulk brittle materials, like PMMA, polystyrene and the thermosetting resins, is explicable in terms of flaws, whilst the theory of Rivlin and Thomas provides a comparable treatment for elastomers. Time and temperature dependence are, in principle, explained in terms of flaw-genesis, the temperature dependence following equation (4.29) well for a variety of synthetic fibres [22] and for cellulose acetate film.[23] As we shall see in the next chapter, however, there are other factors to take into account in considering time and temperature effects. The decrease of brittle fracture strength with increasing temperature discussed in Chapter 2 can also be accounted for in terms of the flaw genesis theory, the ability of cracks to grow to the critical size for catastrophic fracture being much reduced at low temperatures. What is unfortunately lacking in much of this work is the critical experimental testing of the theories available to establish them on a quantitative basis.

Although in principle the flaw theory takes plastic and other non-elastic fracture processes into account it is seldom that such processes can be treated entirely as initiation-controlled. Thus whilst the tensile fracture of PMMA and polystyrene can be regarded in this fashion, all fracture involving non-brittle behaviour of the specimen as a whole must be considered as 'propagation-controlled'. Inelastic deformation in the bulk of the material will have the effect of blunting cracks and flaws so that fracture occurs by tearing rather then by brittle cracking. The result is that no catastrophic phase of fracture occurs and the propagation of the crack becomes significant both in terms of the time and the stress required to cause fracture. For similar reasons the flaw theory provides little information about the brittle-ductile transition.

References

1. BUCHDAHL, R. *J. Polym. Sci.*, **28**, 239 (1958).
2. COTTRELL, A. H. *Proc. R. Soc.*, *A*, **282**, 2 (1964).
3. MARK, H. *Cellulose and its Derivatives* (ed. E. Ott), p. 1001, Interscience Publishers (1943).
4. VINCENT, P. I. *Proc. R. Soc.*, *A*, **282**, 113 (1964).
5. MARSH, D. M. *Fracture of Solids* (ed. D. C. Drucker and J. J. Gilman), p. 143, Interscience Publishers (1963).
6. INGLIS, C. E. *Trans. Inst. Naval Architects, Lond.*, **60**, 219 (1913).
7. GRIFFITH, A. A. *Phil. Trans. R. Soc.*, *A*, **221**, 163 (1921).
8. SACK, R. A. *Proc. Phys. Soc.*, **58**, 729 (1946).
9. SNEDDON, I. N. *Proc. R. Soc.*, *A*, **187**, 229 (1946).
10. SWEDLOW, J. L. *GALCIT Report No. SM* 62–16. Calif. Inst. Technol. (1962).
11. SNEDDON, I. N. *Min. of Supply Armament Res. Dept.* Survey 2/45.
12. BERRY, J. P. *J. Polym. Sci.*, **50**, 313 (1961).
13. BUECHE, A. M., and BERRY, J. P. *Fracture* (ed. B. L. Averbach), p. 265, John Wiley and Sons, Inc. (1959).
14. RIVLIN, R. S., and THOMAS, A. G. *J. Polym. Sci.*, **10**, 291 (1953).
15. OROWAN, E. *Proceedings of the Symposium on Fatigue and Fracture of Metals*, p. 139, John Wiley and Sons, Inc. (1950).
16. GREENSMITH, H. W. *J. appl. Polym. Sci.*, **7**, 993 (1963).
17. THOMAS, A. G. *J. appl. Polym. Sci.*, **3**, 168 (1960).
18. HUTTON, J. F. *Proc. R. Soc.*, *A*, **287**, 222 (1965).
19. BERRY, J. P. *J. Polym. Sci.*, *A*, **1**, 993 (1963).
20. CHARLES R. J. *Fracture* (ed. B. L. Averbach), p. 225, John Wiley and Sons, Inc. (1959).
21. (i) TAYLOR, N. W. *J. appl. Phys.*, **18**, 943 (1947).
— (ii) STUART, H. A., and ANDERSON, O. L. *J. Amer. Ceram. Soc.*, **36**, 416 (1953).
22 BUSSE, W. F., *et al. J. appl. Phys.*, **11**, 769 (1940).
23. HAWARD, R. N. *Trans. Faraday Soc.*, **39**, 267 (1943).

CHAPTER 5

Propagation of Fracture

In the previous chapter fracture was considered to take place catastrophically once certain conditions had been established. The process was 'initiation controlled' and the strength parameters for a material, such as breaking stress, breaking strain, fracture energy and time-to-fracture, were all regarded as being determined by the initiation phase. The question arises, however, as to whether this picture provides a full account of fracture, i.e., whether it is correct to ignore the effect of the propagation phase upon fracture parameters. In this chapter we shall first of all consider the propagation of an established crack through a material and then consider how far propagation must be taken into account in those fracture phenomena which involve both initiation and propagation.

5.1 CONTROLLED FRACTURE

If a small edge crack is made in a specimen of a brittle material and the specimen is loaded till it breaks, the propagation of the initial crack will take place rapidly and in an uncontrolled manner much as in the case of a tensile fracture. Such an experiment can only give information about conditions for initiation as in the case of Berry's work discussed in Chapter 4. It is possible, however, to design an experiment in which the propagation of a crack takes place in a controlled manner. The requirements are simply that the quantity $-(\partial \mathscr{E}/\partial A)_l$ which features in the Griffith, and Rivlin and Thomas theories, and which governs the supply of energy to a propagating fracture should either remain constant or else decrease with increasing crack length c. For an edge crack, as used by Berry, and for a Griffith crack we have seen that $(\partial \mathscr{E}/\partial A)_l$ is proportional to c; but for the pure-shear test-piece of Rivlin and Thomas it is in fact independent of c. A crack in the latter form of test-piece should therefore have no reason to accelerate since the energy supply remains constant as the crack grows.

Truly stable or controlled fracture is obtained, however, only when $-(\partial \mathscr{E}/\partial A)_{l}$ decreases with crack length. This means that provided a crack requires a constant energy supply for continued growth, it will in fact only grow as long as the total stored energy in the specimen is increasing, i.e., as long as external work is being performed. A variety of experimental arrangements have been found to satisfy this requirement for controlled fracture.

The first of these is the cone fracture produced by an indenter forced against a plane surface (Fig. 5.1), a system which has been used

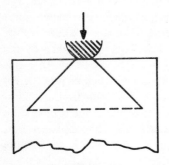

FIG. 5.1   Cone fracture in a glass block.

extensively to study the fracture behaviour of glass.[1] The fracture occurs under tensile stresses set up in accordance with the classical stress distribution determined by Hertz.[2] As the force on the indenter increases so the cone crack penetrates further into the specimen. This method has not been used for polymeric materials since it involves large concentrated compressive forces at the indenter which cause plastic flow and vitiate the classically derived equations for the stress distribution. A second and more useful method was designed by Benbow and Roesler.[3] They used a split beam of the material under examination as shown in Fig. 5.2, the crack being caused to propagate by applying a force F to the split end of the beam as shown. The split arms A may be regarded as cantilevers and the energy stored in them when the free end of the crack is opened by a small distance δ may be calculated in terms of the Young's modulus E of the material. Thence an expression for $(\partial \mathscr{E}/\partial A)_{l}$ is derived, the result being

$$-\left(\frac{\partial \mathscr{E}}{\partial A}\right)_{1} = \frac{3E\delta^{2}b^{3}}{64c^{4}} \tag{5.1}$$

where b is the width of the specimen beam and c is the crack length. It is immediately clear that the dependence on c^{-4} makes the crack very stable and only capable of growth if δ is continuously increased. In practice it was found that a small longitudinal compression was required to keep the crack from turning aside and breaking off one of the cantilever arms but the error involved in introducing this additional constraint is estimated to be less than 1 per cent for PMMA specimens 3 in. wide and $\frac{1}{4}$ in. thick such as were studied by Benbow and Roesler. Berry [4] used a groove to constrain the crack to run longitudinally down the specimen, and also pointed out a possible source of error in Benbow and Roesler's calculations, namely that the

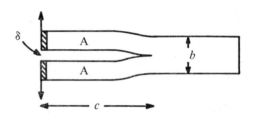

FIG. 5.2 Split beam test piece.

cantilevers are not rigidly mounted at their 'fixed' ends. To overcome this latter difficulty Berry used the expression,

$$\left(\frac{\partial \mathscr{E}}{\partial A}\right)_1 = -\frac{nF\delta}{2cw} \tag{5.2}$$

where F is the force applied to propagate the crack, w is the thickness of the specimen and n is an empirically determined parameter. The cleavage technique has been used by other authors to measure $\mathscr{T}$ in PMMA, polystyrene and certain polyesters, and their results are summarised below together with those of Benbow and Roesler. ($\mathscr{T}$, it will be remembered, is the value $-(\partial \mathscr{E}/\partial A)_1$ at which propagation of the crack takes place.)

These results compare very closely with those given on page 121 for the critical values $\mathscr{T}$ required to initiate fracture in these materials and it thus appears that the energies required for slow propagation and for initiation are identical. This is to be expected, of course, provided that the original crack propagates with no change of geometry, but in non-brittle materials this simple situation does not always hold good. Since two different methods give essentially the same values for $\mathscr{T}$ this quantity can be thought of as a constant for

TABLE 5.1

Characteristic Energies for Crack Propagation

	Material	$\mathscr{T}$ erg cm^{-2}	
Benbow and Roesler [3]	PMMA	$4{\cdot}9 \times 10^5$	
	Polystyrene	$2{\cdot}5 \times 10^6$	slow cracks
	Polystyrene	$3{\cdot}0 \times 10^5$	fast cracks
Svennson [5]	PMMA	$4{\cdot}4 \times 10^5$	
	Polystyrene	$8{\cdot}8 \times 10^5$	
Berry [4]	PMMA	$1{\cdot}4 \times 10^5$	
	Polystyrene	$7{\cdot}1 \times 10^5$	
Broutman and McGarry [6]	PMMA	$1{\cdot}3 \times 10^5$	
	Polystyrene	$4{\cdot}0 \times 10^5$	
	Polyester	$1{\cdot}2 \times 10^4$	

the material at a given speed of cracking and at a given temperature. These last provisos are important, for the figures given above indicate a fall in $\mathscr{T}$ with increasing rate of cracking in polystyrene, and work on elastomers, to be discussed presently, shows that $\mathscr{T}$ can vary

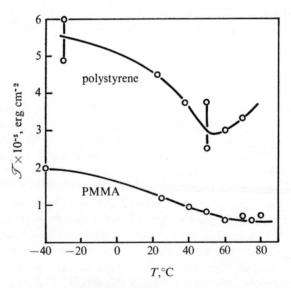

FIG. 5.3   Dependence of characteristic fracture energy upon temperature for polystyrene (upper curve) and PMMA (lower curve) (after Broutman and McGarry[6]).

rapidly as the ambient conditions change. This is not unexpected since most of the energy of propagation is used in plastic or visco-elastic deformation of the highly stressed material at the crack tip and these modes of deformation are strongly influenced by changes in rate and temperature. The variation of $\mathcal{T}$ with temperature for PMMA and polystyrene is shown in Fig. 5.3.

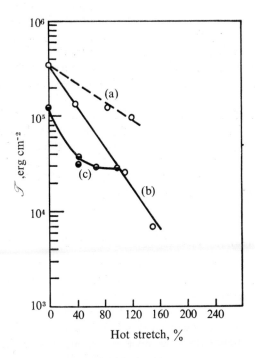

FIG. 5.4   Effect of molecular orientation upon char-acteristic fracture energy. (a) polystyrene oriented at 143°C, (b) polystyrene oriented at 116°C, (c) PMMA oriented at 124°C (after Broutman and McGarry[8]).

Just as $\mathcal{T}$ varies in magnitude from polymer to polymer, so does it vary for a given polymer with such things as the degree of cross-linking and molecular anistropy. The results given above refer to uncross-linked materials but it is found [6] that the introduction of cross links into PMMA causes a reduction of $\mathcal{T}$ as follows:

PMMA	$\mathscr{T}$ erg cm^{-2}
uncross-linked	$1 \cdot 3 \times 10^5$
lightly cross-linked	$8 \cdot 0 \times 10^4$
densely cross-linked	$2 \cdot 3 \times 10^4$

This reduction reflects the reduction of plasticity in cross-linked materials and is accompanied by the disappearance of interference colours from the fracture surface (see Chapter 6) which arise in uncross-linked material from a plastically deformed surface layer.[7] The value of $\mathscr{T}$ for the densely cross-linked PMMA is typical of the more common thermosetting resins, i.e., roughly a factor of ten smaller than for an uncross-linked polymer. It is still, however, a factor of 100 greater than the true surface energy so that even in a thermosetting resin considerable plastic flow must occur at the crack tip.

The effect of molecular orientation has also been studied [8] and Fig. 5.4 shows $\mathscr{T}$ as a function of the percentage hot-stretch for polystyrene, the crack being propagated along the direction of pre-orientation. The characteristic energy for oriented material may be as little as one hundredth of that for the isotropic polymer, a value as low as 7000 erg cm^{-2} being obtained.

5.2 Characteristic Fracture Energy in Elastomers

Using a non-crystallising, unfilled vulcanised rubber such as SBR, steady crack propagation can be obtained using either of the test pieces described in Chapter 4 as well as others described by Thomas.[9] In rubbers and ductile materials controlled propagation of a crack may be obtained not only by virtue of a suitable geometrical arrangement such as that of Benbow and Roesler, but also by virtue of the strong rate-dependence of the parameter $\mathscr{T}$. Generally speaking the energy required to produce a given non-elastic deformation increases with the rate of attainment of that deformation, so that a fast crack requires greater energy (higher $\mathscr{T}$ value) than a slow one. Acceleration of a crack, even when favoured by the geometry, may therefore be prevented and the growing crack is inherently stable.

The characteristic tearing energy has been measured [10] as a function of rate of crack propagation and temperature for gum SBR and the results are presented in the three-dimensional plot of Fig. 5.5. Its value ranges from more than 10^7 erg cm^{-2} at low temperatures and high rates to 10^5 erg cm^{-2} at high temperatures and low rates. Tests over a wider range of experimental conditions suggest that at extremely low rates of propagation the value of $\mathcal{T}$ may approach within a factor of ten the actual surface energy of the material so fulfilling quite closely the Griffith energy balance. No *plastic* deformation occurs at the tip in these materials, but every volume element in the path of the propagating crack is subjected to a stress-strain cycle (cf. Chapter 2) as the crack approaches and recedes from its vicinity, and energy is dissipated visco-elastically during this strain

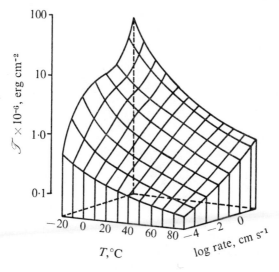

FIG. 5.5 Characteristic fracture energy in gum SBR (after Greensmith and Thomas[10]).

cycle. The slower the cycle or the higher the temperature the less energy is dissipated and this clearly explains the form of the time-temperature dependence of $\mathcal{T}$. The WLF equation may be applied to $\mathcal{T}$ giving a master curve [11] from which its value at any rate or temperature may be deduced (Fig. 5.6). A useful approximation to the dependence of $\mathcal{T}$ upon the rate of propagation at a given temperature is the equation $dc/dt = q\mathcal{T}^n$ where n has the value of about 4 for SBR rubber and q is a function of temperature.

Greensmith [12] extended the measurements of $\mathcal{T}$ from the 'simple' styrenebutadiene rubbers having neither filler nor crystallinity, to carbon-reinforced materials and to natural rubber which undergoes strain-crystallisation, and the results for typical cases are shown in Figs. 5.7 and 5.8. An important distinction arises, however, between these $\mathscr{T}$ values and those for SBR in that the crack in the complex rubbers does not generally propagate smoothly at a constant speed but proceeds in a stick-slip manner. The $\mathscr{T}$ values recorded are the

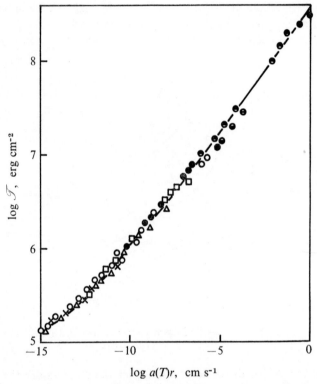

FIG. 5.6 WLF master curve for characteristic fracture energy in gum SBR (after Mullins[11]).

maximum values, appropriate to the 'stick' phase of the process, and are thus strictly associated with initiation events rather than propagation. The reason for this behaviour will appear presently. The outstanding feature of the new results is the appearance of a 'plateau' region in the three-dimensional plot superimposed on the basic behaviour pattern of the SBR. This is most clearly seen in the case of an SBR filled with fine thermal black (Fig. 5.7) where both the original visco-elastic dissipation pattern and the plateau are visible. In a strain-crystallising rubber (Fig. 5.8) the plateau extends over almost the whole experimental range but the basic behaviour reappears at

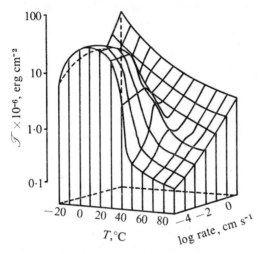

FIG. 5.7. Characteristic fracture energy in an SBR vulcanisate containing fine thermal carbon black (after Greensmith[12]).

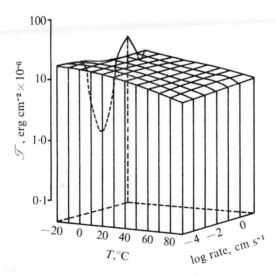

FIG. 5.8 Characteristic fracture energy in gum natural rubber (after Greensmith[12]).

low temperatures and high speeds where it may be supposed that crystallisation does not develop rapidly enough to exert its full effect. Outside the plateau regions, $\mathscr{T}$ may fall to a value similar to that for unreinforced SBR and the fracture is no longer stick-slip.

The effect of the plateau regions is profound in that $\mathscr{T}$ is increased by factors as high as 10^3 over the corresponding value for the unreinforced rubber and we shall see presently how this can be used to explain the difference in tensile and other strength properties brought about by crystallisation or particulate fillers. It also emphasises, however, that reinforcement is only effective over certain ranges of rate and temperature so that modes of rupture, such as wear, in which extremes of rate and temperature are encountered, may be relatively little affected by reinforcement.

The cause of the plateau regions in the $\mathscr{T}$/rate/temperature diagrams is a matter of great interest. Basically it can be said that the extra energy per unit area of crack interface, over and above that due to visco-elastic deformation as in SBR, is contributed by mechanical hysteresis arising from non-visco-elastic causes. In filled rubbers this is probably due to breakdown between the filler and the rubber in a highly stressed region surrounding the crack tip whilst in strain-crystallising rubbers it is due to the energy lost as heat of crystallisation. Stick-slip behaviour of the crack occurs because these forms of energy dissipation, unlike visco-elastic losses, tend to decrease in magnitude with increasing crack velocity and propagation is thus unstable. To say this, however, is not to tell the whole story of how these non-visco-elastic contributions affect propagation for it is found that *some* small-scale propagation of the crack occurs at values of $-(\partial\mathscr{E}/\partial A)_1$ smaller than $\mathscr{T}$ ('slip'). In fact for natural rubber it has been found [13] that small-scale propagation obeys the law,

$$\left.\begin{array}{r} \Delta c \simeq p(\partial\mathscr{E}/\partial A)_1^2 \\ -(\partial\mathscr{E}/\partial A)_1 < \mathscr{T}\,(\text{'slip'}) \end{array}\right\} \qquad (5.3)$$

for

Δc is the amount of crack growth and p is a constant. It is thus seen that the high $\mathscr{T}$ values obtained in the plateau regions do not reflect an intrinsic resistance to fracture such that more work must be done at the tip to initiate fracture, since propagation commences at the lowest observable $\mathscr{T}$ values as in SBR. Whereas in SBR however propagation continues at low $\mathscr{T}$ values, albeit slowly, the crack in the complex material travels a small distance Δc and stops. Further propagation can then only be obtained by increasing the forces on the test-piece, i.e., by increasing the total energy of the system so that $-(\partial \mathscr{E}/\partial A)_l$ also rises. This process continues until Δc has increased to a critical value [14] which in gum natural rubber is about 50 μm but can be up to 1 cm in some carbon filled rubbers. At this point the 'slip' phase of fracture occurs and the crack propagates rapidly for some distance.

The high resistance to fracture displayed in the plateau regions is thus clearly due to the inhibition of propagation after its commencement and the reason for this inhibition is of great interest. Before we can explain it, however, it will be necessary to consider the distribution of stress at a crack. This is done generally in the following section and we shall return to the case of an elastomer later in the chapter.

5.3 THE DISTRIBUTION OF STRESS AROUND A CRACK TIP

The variation of fracture energy with the conditions of test and with the state of the material, whilst they do not prevent $\mathscr{T}$ being a useful parameter by which to characterise fracture, do pose the question of its physical significance. We have already said that $\mathscr{T}$ represents the dissipation of energy at the tip of a crack but is it possible to go further and relate it to better-defined quantities such as yield in elastic-plastic solids or mechanical hysteresis in viscoelastic ones? Fortunately some progress has been made in this direction but in order to explain this it will be necessary to discuss first of all the distributions of stress and strain in the vicinity of a crack. In Chapter 4 reference was made to the classical elastic solution of Inglis and to Griffith's use of it in deriving his fracture criterion. It will now be necessary to deal with this matter more explicitly.

(i) *Case of an ideally elastic material*

The distribution of stress around a crack in an infinite elastic lamella has been widely studied and the solutions provided by infinitesimal strain theory are well known. These solutions begin, with Inglis,[15] by considering the crack to be an elongated elliptical hole with finite tip radius and this case has been treated, for various loading conditions, by many authors.[16-19] The limiting case of a slit of zero width has been calculated by Westergaard [20] and by Sneddon,[21] but since such a crack has zero tip radius, the theory predicts infinite stresses at the tip, a result which is not of great usefulness in establishing fracture criteria. This dilemma was resolved in part by Elliott [22]

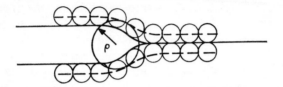

FIG. 5.9   Atomistic picture of a cleavage crack.

who pointed out that because of the atomistic nature of matter there could be no material closer than the atomic radius to the mathematical point representing the tip (Fig. 5.9). Maximum stresses on a plane of atoms this distance away from the mathematical line representing the crack are predicted to be finite and of a sensible magnitude.

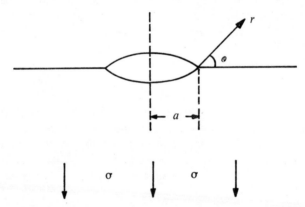

FIG. 5.10   Stresses at a crack, equation 5·4: The x-axis is the horizontal or crack axis.

Of the various results available perhaps the most versatile for our present purpose are those given by Irwin [23] and based upon Westergaard's stress-function solutions. The situation treated is shown in Fig. 5.10 and the various stresses are given by the following expressions valid for values of $r/a \ll 1$, i.e., for the region close to the tip.

$$\sigma_x = \mathcal{K}(2r)^{-\frac{1}{2}} \cos{(\theta/2)}(1 - \sin{\theta/2} \sin{3\theta/2}) - \sigma_{0x}$$

$$\sigma_y = \mathcal{K}(2r)^{-\frac{1}{2}} \cos{(\theta/2)}(1 + \sin{\theta/2} \sin{3\theta/2})$$

$$\sigma_z = \mathcal{K}2\mu(2r)^{-\frac{1}{2}} \cos{\theta/2} - \mu\sigma_{0x} \text{ [plane strain]}$$

$$= 0 \text{ [plane stress]}$$

$$\tau_{xy} = \mathcal{K}(2r)^{-\frac{1}{2}} \cos{\theta/2} \sin{\theta/2} \cos{3\theta/2}$$

$$\tau_{yz} = \tau_{zx} = 0 \tag{5.4}$$

Where σ_x, σ_y, σ_z and τ_{xy}, τ_{yz}, τ_{zx} are the direct and shear stresses respectively, r and θ are polar co-ordinates with origin at the crack tip, and $\mathcal{K}$ and σ_{0x} are stress field parameters. Of these, σ_{0x} is at most points small and can be neglected leaving $\mathcal{K}$ the only parameter to relate the magnitude of the local stress at a given point to the applied stress field and the geometry of the crack. The nature of the parameter $\mathcal{K}$ is best seen by giving a few examples. For a large plate, width D containing a central slit of length $2a$ and loaded by a uniform tensile stress σ_0 normal to the crack axis [24]

$$\mathcal{K} = \sigma_0(\pi D \tan{\pi a/D})^{\frac{1}{2}} \tag{5.5}$$

If $D \gg a$ this tends to the case of an infinite plate or sheet and

$$\mathcal{K} = \pi\sigma_0 a^{\frac{1}{2}}. \tag{5.6}$$

Equations (5.5) and (5.6) also apply sufficiently well for an edge crack of length a. Some actual values for the various stresses in the neighbourhood of a crack have been calculated by Cook and Gordon [25] and are shown in Figs. 5.11 and 5.12.

(ii) *Stress distribution and fracture criteria*

In Chapter 4 two criteria were advanced for fracture in perfectly elastic materials, namely the critical stress criterion and the Griffith energy balance theory. Both of these criteria can be expressed in terms involving the parameter $\mathcal{K}$ as will now be shown. Firstly the critical stress criterion supposes that fracture will occur when the maximum stress at the tip of a pre-existent flaw or crack achieves some critical value. For a crack of length $2a$ and tip radius ρ it was shown that the maximum tip stress is

$$\sigma_y = 2\sigma_0(a/\rho)^{\frac{1}{2}} \tag{4.6}$$

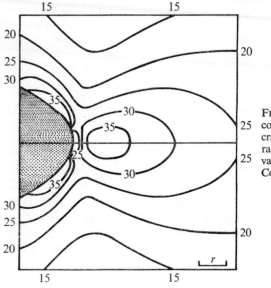

FIG. 5.11 Iso-stress contours near a crack tip of finite radius r showing values of σ_x/σ_0 (after Cook and Gordon[25]).

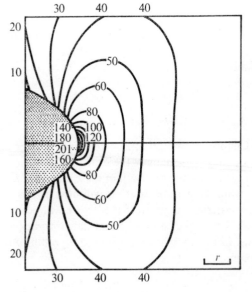

FIG. 5.12 Iso-stress contours near a crack tip of finite radius r showing values of σ_y/σ_0 (after Cook and Gordon[25]).

From equation (5.4), however, the maximum stress at the boundary of a crack tip of finite curvature ρ is given by setting $\theta = 0$ and $r = \rho$,

$$\sigma_y = \mathcal{K}(2\rho)^{-\frac{1}{2}}$$

$$= \frac{\pi\sigma_0}{\sqrt{2}}\left(\frac{a}{\rho}\right)^{\frac{1}{2}} \tag{5.7}$$

$$\simeq 2 \cdot 2\sigma_0(a/\rho)^{\frac{1}{2}} \tag{5.8}$$

a result identical (except for a small numerical factor) with that of equation (4.6). It is thus possible to phrase the critical stress criterion in terms of $\mathcal{K}$ by saying that for a crack of given geometry, fracture will occur when a critical value of $\mathcal{K}$ is achieved. Mathematically this is expressed from equation (5.7) by

$$\mathcal{K}_c = \sigma_{max}(2\rho)^{\frac{1}{2}}.$$

It is also possible to express the Griffith fracture criterion in terms of $\mathcal{K}$. From equation (4.11) we know that the rate of decay of elastic stored energy in a plate due to crack growth is

$$\frac{\partial}{\partial a}\left(\frac{\pi\sigma_0^2 a^2}{E}\right) = \frac{2\pi\sigma_0^2 a}{E}$$

but from equation (5.6) this is equal to

$$2\mathcal{K}^2/\pi E$$

for the case considered, i.e., a crack in an infinite lamina under a tensile load perpendicular to the crack axis. Applying the energy balance criterion we thus find, for fracture,

$$2\mathcal{K}^2/\pi E \geqslant 4S$$

or in terms of a critical value of $\mathcal{K}$,

$$\mathcal{K}_c^2 = 2\pi E S. \tag{5.9}$$

The foregoing discussion shows again the essential equivalence of the two criteria since both can be expressed in terms of the attainment of a critical value for $\mathcal{K}$. The wider usefulness of the stress field parameter however lies not so much in a restatement of the criteria of Chapter 4 but in handling the more difficult problems of inelastic materials.

(iii) *Fracture criteria in elastic-plastic solids*

Most real materials depart from ideally elastic behaviour before they fracture and it follows that there will exist in these cases a region close

11

to the crack tip in which plastic or other inelastic deformations have occurred and in which therefore the stress distribution of equation (5.4) will not apply. Provided, however, that this region is a small area contained within a plastic-elastic boundary at some distance $r = r_p$ from the crack tip we can suppose that the elastic solution holds for all regions $r > r_p$ and treat the crack as being simply blunted to this extent. The propagation of the crack must now be governed by the propagation of the plastic zone and a crude criterion will be obtained simply by setting the maximum stress at the boundary of this zone (i.e., at $r = r_p$) equal to the tensile yield stress Y of the material. Thus the crack will propagate if

$$\sigma_y(r_p, \theta = 0) = Y$$
$$\mathscr{K}_c(2r_p)^{-\frac{1}{2}} = Y. \tag{5.10}$$

This equation shows that the critical value of $\mathscr{K}$ required to propagate a plastic-elastic crack will depend both upon the yield stress of the material and the size of the plastic zone. Generalising the relationship between $\mathscr{K}$ and surface energy derived above (equation (5.9)) to read

$$\mathscr{K}_c^2 = 2\pi E \mathscr{T} \tag{5.11}$$

as is appropriate to the present case where energy in crack propagation is dissipated in plastic deformation, we fined that the characteristic fracture energy $\mathscr{T}$ is, like $\mathscr{K}$, dependent directly upon the yield stress and the size of the plastic zone.

The yield stress can be considered a material constant, but the second parameter, r_p is not a property of the material as such and it is not at once obvious what does determine it. It will itself depend in an inverse manner upon the yield stress, but not the yield stress in simple tension since the state of stress at its boundaries will in general be triaxial. It would seem possible to say in general that $\mathscr{T}$ is a function only of $[Y]$, this symbol denoting a set of yield criteria for the conditions applying at the tip. Two specially important cases will be briefly mentioned.

Firstly it is possible that $[Y]$ is a function of time, and this is a situation we would expect in polymeric materials. The longer the application of stress the lower will $[Y]$ become and the value of $\mathscr{T}$ will vary accordingly. The incorporation of such a time effect into the theory is mathematically complex and will not be further considered here.

The second possibility is that [Y] will change in value according to the state of stress at the tip of the crack and since this will vary with the thickness of the lamina containing the crack, a plate-thickness effect might be expected. In a very thick plate a state approaching plane strain will obtain since the component of stress σ_z normal to the plane of the plate builds up from a zero value on the plate surfaces to a maximum value at its centre. In a very thick plate most of the through-thickness will therefore be subject to significant stresses in

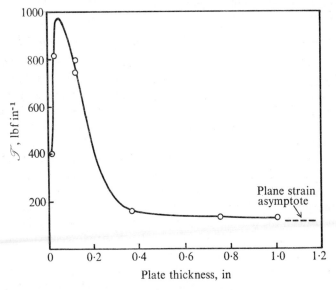

FIG. 5.13 Dependence of characteristic fracture energy upon plate thickness in an aluminium alloy (after Irwin[26]).

the z direction. Yield under these conditions will occur only at high direct stresses and the extent of plastic deformation will be more limited (at a given overall stress level) than it would otherwise be. The energy dissipated in fracture propagation under plane strain conditions might be *smaller* because r_p is smaller, but it might alternatively be *greater* because [Y] is greater. In fact experience shows that in some metals $\mathscr{T}$ is smaller for thick plates indicating that the limitation to r_p is the more important factor.

In a thin plate σ_z never achieves significant proportions and plane stress conditions (i.e., $\sigma_z = 0$) are approximated. [Y] is lower than for plane strain, r_p is larger and an increase in $\mathscr{T}$ is sometimes observed. Fig. 5.13 shows the effect of thickness upon $\mathcal{T}$ for an aluminium alloy.[26] However, such thickness effects are not always found and no reliable evidence for them has been reported to date for polymeric materials. Although, therefore, the thickness effect militates against the concept of $\mathcal{T}$ as a 'material constant' it need not cause undue concern since its influence is not great in many materials and its origin is, in general terms, understood. Providing the conditions of fracture are defined $\mathcal{T}$ remains a characteristic parameter which provides quantitative information on fracture in a given material.

(iv) *Stress distribution and fracture in an inhomogeneous material*

A general discussion of this subject lies beyond our scope but two cases of interest are considered here. The first is that of a material containing a dispersion of inclusions, considered for simplicity to be spheres. If the inclusions are sufficiently small for a number of them to lie in the highly stressed region surrounding the crack tip their presence becomes important. Any discontinuity of elastic properties in a uniform stress field will cause re-distribution of stress or 'stress concentrations'. The magnitude of stress concentration at a spherical particle of infinite stiffness embedded in a uniform matrix is two: i.e., the maximum stress at or near the particle surface is twice that which would exist if the particle were absent. The stress concentrations due to particles in the stress field of a crack are therefore superimposed upon that due to the crack itself and the breaking stress of the material (or matrix-particle interface, whichever is weaker) is attained at points removed from the free surface of the crack. Internal breakdown thus occurs giving rise to propagating secondary fractures which may or may not link up with the primary fracture. The process of secondary fracture is considered further in Chapter 6. Another, and perhaps more important consequence of internal rupture at dispersed particles is that at each point of secondary fracture some elastically stored energy is lost. If there occurs multiple internal breakdown in advance of the propagating crack a large quantity of energy may be dissipated in a quasi-plastic manner, and it is likely that this process contributes to the high $\mathcal{T}$ value found in elastomers filled with colloidal carbon black.

The second case of interaction between the stress distribution and structure of the material concerns situations where lines of weakness or 'fault planes' are present. Cook and Gordon[25] considered a crack propagating through a lamellar material in a direction normal to the lamellae and pointed out that the component of stress σ_x directed along the crack axis, which is usually ignored in fracture criteria because its value at the free surface of the tip is zero, is capable of opening up fissures ahead of the crack (Fig. 5.14). Such a fissure would effectively blunt the crack and hinder any further progress.

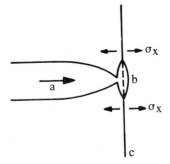

FIG. 5.14   Stopping of a primary crack (a) by a secondary crack (b) opened on a plane of weakness (c) (after Cook and Gordon[25]).

They suggest that this mechanism is operative in any material with a lamellar or fibre structure and may explain the high strength of such materials when stressed *along* the fibre or lamellar directions.

The interaction of the stress distribution with the structure of materials is likely to prove of great importance in polymeric solids where such complex microstructures are encountered and it may be impossible to explain fully the behaviour of semi-crystalline and other two-phase materials without some appeal to this effect.

(v) *Stress distribution and propagation in elastomers*

A situation of special interest arises in the case of materials, notably elastomers, which display mechanical hysteresis rather than plastic flow when subject to finite strain. The distribution of stress around a crack in an elastomer cannot, of course, be calculated by classical elasticity theory, since both the requirements of Hookean behaviour and infinitesimal strain are violated. Photoelastic techniques have however been used [27] to measure the stress distribution experimentally in a rubberlike material and, apart from an overall distortion of the map of principal stress directions, the situation proves to be qualitatively similar to that in a rigid material. That is to say (see Fig. 5.12) the major principal stress σ_y decays rapidly along the crack axis from a maximum at the tip to its value in the bulk of the sheet whilst at the same time the axial stress σ_x rises from zero at the tip to a maximum some distance along the axis. Near the crack tip the maximum value of σ_y is found at $y = 0$, i.e., on the axis of the crack, but further away the maximum stresses are found to either side of the axis. It is possible, then, to draw two symmetrically disposed 'maximum stress loci' which coincide on axis near the tip but curve away to either side of the axis as x increases (Fig. 5.15).

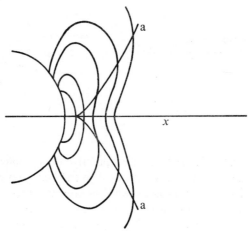

FIG. 5.15   Iso-stress contours (σ_y) and maximum stress
trajectories (a) near a crack tip.

When a crack propagates, its stress distribution usually moves with it so that the locus of maximum stress (along which, of course, fracture will always occur) coincides with the crack axis. This is why cracks in a uniform field of force propagate in a straight line. If for some reason, however, the stress distribution set up at an initially stationary crack fails to move with the crack when the latter propagates, the growing crack will follow, not the axis but one or both of the loci of maximum stress giving deviation or forking of the crack tip. This is what appears to happen in the small-scale propagation of a crack in reinforced rubbers,[14] the crack curving away from the axis as it grows, in a highly reproducible manner (Fig. 5.16). A second consequence of a 'stationary stress distribution' is that the growing crack will encounter lower and lower stresses as it proceeds and must therefore come to a halt unless the overall stress on the specimen is increased to compensate. Thus the two main features of 'small scale' propagation in reinforced rubbers, deviation from the axis and crack inhibition, are both readily explained on this hypothesis. When at some high overall stress the mechanisms maintaining the 'stationary' distribution gives way, the stress in the test piece will be far in excess of that necessary for propagation and a catastrophic phase of the fracture will ensue. Stick-slip fracture is thus also accounted for.

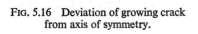

FIG. 5.16   Deviation of growing crack
from axis of symmetry.

Experiments have shown [28] that this theory is essentially correct for reinforced rubbers and have also shown how mechanical hysteresis can give rise to the phenomenon of a stationary stress distribution. It is possible that the same basic concept may account for crack forking and deviation at high speeds in more perfectly elastic materials when the crack velocity approaches the speed of propagation of sound (i.e., of the stress waves themselves) and a theoretical treatment using only classical elasticity theory does in fact predict off-axis maximum stresses under these circumstances.[29]

5.4 CREEP FRACTURE AND TENSILE STRENGTH IN ELASTOMERS

As has been emphasised before, all forms of fracture involve the initiation of cracks and their propagation through a material. If the material is brittle, crack propagation is catastrophic in a tensile test and the tensile strength, breaking strain and so on are governed by the initiation phase of the fracture. In ductile or hysteresial materials, however, such as concern us in the present section, this is no longer true and the propagation phase becomes all important.

(i) Crack growth theory for non-crystallising elastomers

Greensmith [30] has advanced a theory which accounts for the tensile and creep fracture behaviour of non-crystallising elastomers purely as a propagation phenomenon.

In such materials it has already been shown that the rate of growth of a crack is given by

$$dc/dt = q\mathcal{T}^n \qquad (5.12)$$

where q is a function of temperature. For an edge crack or similar flaw

$$\mathscr{T} = KcW \qquad (4.22)$$

whence

$$dc/dt = q(KcW)^n. \qquad (5.13)$$

Fracture is now assumed to occur by the growth of pre-existent flaws of effective length c_0 so that integration of equation (5.13) gives immediately the time to break under the imposed conditions. Two cases are considered.

(a) *Test piece held at constant extension* (*creep fracture test*)

In this case W and K are constants and the time to break is

$$t_f = \frac{1}{q} \int_{c_0}^{c} \frac{dc}{(KcW)^n}$$

or

$$t_f = \{q(n-1)K^n W^n\}^{-1} \left(\frac{1}{c_0^{n-1}} - \frac{1}{c^{n-1}} \right).$$

Allowing that c, the crack length at fracture, greatly exceeds c_0 we have

$$t_f = \{q(n-1)K^n W^n c_0^{n-1}\}^{-1} \qquad (5.14)$$

W is the value of the stored energy density at the strain imposed.

(b) *Test piece extended at uniform rate* (*tensile test*)

The strain is given by

$$\varepsilon = vt$$

where v is the rate of extension. We assume that the stored energy density W is related to the strain by an equation of the form

$$W = B\varepsilon^p = B(vt)^p$$

where B and p are fitting constants. Integration of equation (5.13) leads to

$$t_f = (pn+1)\{q(n-1)K^n W^n c_0^{n-1}\}^{-1} \qquad (5.15)$$

W again referring to the point of fracture.

Equations (5.14) and (5.15) require modification to allow for the fact that equation (5.12) only holds true up to a certain value $\mathscr{T}_c$ of

$\mathscr{T}$ beyond which dc/dt increases very rapidly. Assuming infinite velocity at $\mathscr{T} > \mathscr{T}_c$ the equations become:

(a) For creep fracture

$$t_f = \frac{1-(Kc_0 W/\mathscr{T}_c)^{n-1}}{q(n-1)(KW)^n c_0^{n-1}}. \tag{5.16}$$

(b) For tensile test

$$t_f = \frac{(pn+1)\{1-(Kc_0 W/\mathscr{T}_c)^{n-1}\}}{q(n-1)(KW)^n c_0^{n-1}}. \tag{5.17}$$

To check the theory experiments were carried out on specimens containing an artificial crack of length c_0 and Figs. 5.17 and 5.18

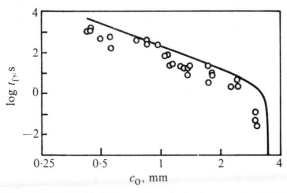

FIG. 5.17   Relation between time to fracture and artificial flaw size in creep fracture in SBR, showing experimental points and (solid line) the theoretical prediction (after Greensmith[30]).

show the measure of agreement obtained between theory and experiment for the dependence respectively of t upon c_0 (in the creep fracture tests) and of t upon W (in both creep fracture and tensile tests). In *actual* tensile and creep fracture experiments, in which c_0 is now the intrinsic flaw size, the theory again works well as shown in Fig. 5.19 for both kinds of test. Although a fitting constant has been used in this case the same value of it is suitable for both the tensile and creep fracture plots.

(ii) *Molecular theories of strength in non-crystallising elastomers*

A number of attempts have been made to predict the tensile strength of these materials, together with their dependence on various parameters such as cross-linking density, temperature and rate, without any appeal to crack propagation phenomena. These theories rely upon some initiation criterion arising from the behaviour of the molecular network. Since all molecular movements in polymers are visco-elastic in nature, the theories are generally successful in predicting that fracture itself will exhibit similar visco-elastic tendencies such as the existence of a 'failure envelope' as discussed in Chapter

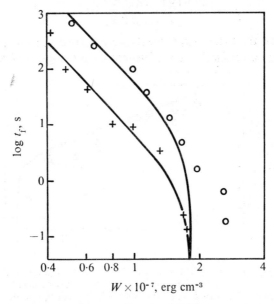

FIG. 5.18 Relation between time to fracture and stored energy density at constant c_0 in SBR. (○) at various uniform extension rates, (+) at constant strain. Solid lines show theoretical predictions (after Greensmith[30]).

2 and the fact that fracture parameters in these materials obey the WLF equation. The theories have been recently reviewed and the reader is referred elsewhere for full details,[31] but we consider here some of the assumptions and predictions involved.

The first step that is often made is the reasonable assumption that the local fracture stress in a polymer network is proportional to the number of effective (i.e., load bearing) network chains crossing unit area. If the density of cross-link points is n per unit volume, then this number will be $n^{2/3}$ so that an increase in fracture strength is predicted with increasing cross-link density. An important proviso here is that the presence of a molecular chain end will reduce the number of effective chains by one so that a factor $(1 - 2M_c/M)$ must be introduced in computing this total. Here M is the molar mass of the material and M_c the molar mass between cross-links. Taylor and Darin [32] pointed out, however, that as cross-linking increases so the elongation to fracture of the network decreases, so that fewer chains are oriented along the axis of strain at the moment of fracture. The

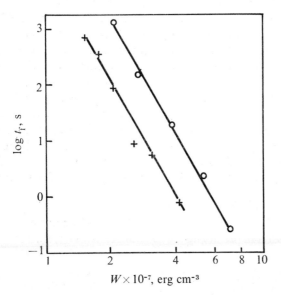

FIG. 5.19   Relation between time to fracture and stored energy density in SBR in actual tensile and creep fracture tests (i.e., no artificial flaws). (O) at various uniform extension rates, (+) at constant strain. Solid lines show theoretical predictions (after Greensmith[30]).

number of effective load-bearing chains is thus reduced with the result that a maximum appears in the graph of fracture stress against cross-link density as previously noted in Chapter 2. A. Bueche [33] proposed a theory predicting the energy to fracture in terms of the form of the stress-strain curve, the cross-linking density and the activation energy for fracture of network chains. In this theory the rupture of network chains is viewed as a thermally activated process and the application of stress to the network is assumed to reduce the activation energy for rupture by an amount equal to the elastic energy stored per network chain. Chain rupture thus becomes statistically more probable than the opposite process of re-linking with a resultant accumulation of damage which, by throwing additional stress on neighbouring, unbroken chains, eventually becomes catastrophic. The theory was successful in predicting the dependence of energy to fracture upon cross-link density in a range of radiation cross-linked polydimethylsiloxane rubbers.

F. Bueche [34] also considered the probability of the rupture of one network chain throwing sufficient extra stress upon neighbouring chains to cause a runaway sequence of fracture. He, however, took into account the wide variation in the chain length between cross-links which is to be expected in any real vulcanisate and like previous theories predicted a maximum in the plot of fracture stress against cross-link density. F. Bueche also used the idea of modifying the activation energy for chain rupture by a term representing the elastic stored energy in the chain. Since the network responds visco-elastically to the applied forces the actual value of the stored energy is a function of time and temperature and the dependence of fracture stress upon these variables is thus a consequence of the theory.

(iii) *Theories of Knauss and Halpin*

Although the molecular theories of fracture in amorphous rubbers are successful in predicting the general behaviour of fracture strength as a function of network parameters and environmental conditions, they are unsatisfactory in neglecting the role of crack propagation. Recently new theories have appeared which combine the statistical approach of the molecular theories with the concept of crack growth. The relationship between these theories and that of Greensmith is, of course, that the former set out to calculate from first principles what Greensmith takes as empirically given: the rate of propagation of a flaw as a function of stress and temperature. Greensmith's theory remains, however, the most realistic as far as crack propagation mechanisms are concerned.

The two theories to be considered here are due respectively to Halpin and to Knauss. Halpin [35] considers the deformation and rupture of network chains at the tip of a growing crack, relating them to the behaviour of the bulk material in the following way. The local stress for rupture at the crack tip σ_1 is related to the macroscopic fracture stress σ_f by a stress concentration factor s,

$$\sigma_1 = s\sigma_f. \qquad (5.18)$$

The 'generalised' creep compliance is defined as

$$\Gamma(t) \equiv \phi(\varepsilon)/\sigma \qquad (5.19)$$

where ε is the strain and ϕ a function, and the time scale t of molecular events at the tip of the crack is supposed to be related to the time t_f for macroscopic fracture according to

$$t = t_f/q \qquad (5.20)$$

where q is a constant. A network chain at the crack tip is assumed to break at some critical strain ε_c giving the local breaking stress

$$\sigma_1 = \phi(\varepsilon_c)/\Gamma(t_f/q) \qquad (5.21)$$

and thus the macroscopic fracture stress is

$$\sigma_f = \phi(\varepsilon_c)/s\Gamma(t_f/q) \equiv \frac{K_0}{\Gamma(t_f/q)} \qquad (5.22)$$

Likewise, from equations (5.19) and (5.22) the macroscopic breaking strain ε_f is such that

$$\phi(\varepsilon_f) = K_0\{\Gamma(t_f)/\Gamma(t_f/q)\}. \qquad (5.23)$$

A theoretical relation with known experimental validity is used for $\phi(\varepsilon)$, and Γ is thus also known from equation (5.19). In Figs. 5.20 and 5.21 the predictions of equations (5.22) and (5.23) are shown as solid lines on plots respectively of σ_f (reduced) and ε_f against t_f, the constants K_0 and q being adjusted to give the best fit with experimental data obtained on SBR rubber.

The theory of Halpin is closely akin to that of Greensmith in considering the propagation of existing flaws. Knauss's theory [36] is different in that it considers the time required to generate flaws of a critical size which thereafter propagate rapidly to cause macroscopic failure. The criterion for critical size is the familiar one that the quantity, Wc where W is the stored energy density in the specimen and c is the radius of a circular crack (of area $A = \pi c^2$) should equal or exceed some critical value

$$WA^{\frac{1}{2}} \geqslant \mathscr{T}. \qquad (5.24)$$

The crack grows to this critical size by the activated rupture of network chains at its tip. The rates of bond breakage and bond reformation are respectively

$$\left.\begin{array}{l} dN_2/dt = -k_{21}N_2 + k_{12}N_1 \\ dN_1/dt = -k_{12}N_1 + k_{21}N_2 \end{array}\right\} \qquad (5.25)$$

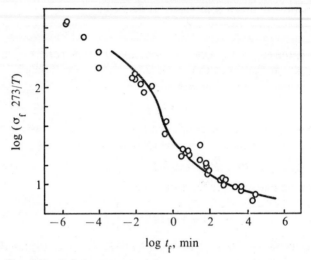

FIG. 5.20 Relation between fracture stress, time to fracture and temperature in SBR. Solid line shows prediction of equation 5.22 (after Halpin[35]).

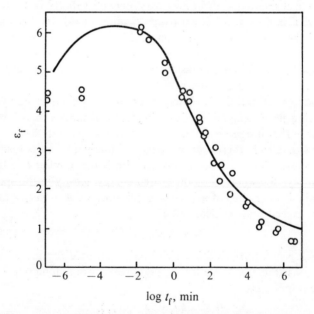

FIG. 5.21 Relation between fracture strain and time to fracture in SBR. Solid line shows prediction of equation 5.23 (after Halpin[35]).

where N_1 is the number of unbroken bonds, N_2 the number of broken bonds ($N_1 + N_2 = N_0$) and k_{12}, k_{21} are the rate constants for the two opposing processes. Assuming the activation energies of the processes are altered by the amount of stored energy in the chain (W/N, where N is the number of chains per unit volume) we have

$$\left. \begin{aligned} k_{12} &= Ba(T) \exp\left(-W/NkT\right) \\ k_{21} &= Ba(T) \exp\left(W/NkT\right) \end{aligned} \right\} \qquad (5.26)$$

where $a(T)$ is a temperature dependent function, whose form is assumed, and B is a constant. The rate of bond breakage and thus the rate of increase in interfacial crack area is obtained by subtraction of equations (5.25) giving

$$(2A_0 Ba(T))^{-1} \frac{dA}{dt} = -\left(\frac{N_2 - N_1}{N_0}\right) \cosh \frac{W}{NkT} + \sinh \frac{W}{NkT} \qquad (5.27)$$

when A_0 is a constant with dimensions of area. But from equation (5.24), at the critical condition (i.e., where the equality applies),

$$\frac{dA}{dt} = -\frac{2\mathscr{T}^2}{W^3} \frac{dW}{dt} \qquad (5.28)$$

so that a relation is established between W, dW/dt and T by equations (5.27) and (5.28). A theoretical relation from linear visco-elastic theory is used to predict the dependence of W upon time and the predicted time to break obtained by integration with respect to time. Using unknown constants B, $\mathscr{T}$ and N to fit his theory to experimental data, Knauss was able to obtain reasonable agreement.

(iv) *Summary of tensile-strength theories for amorphous elastomers*

These theories are at first sight rather confusing because they all appear to succeed in predicting experimental data although all begin from different and sometimes contradictory assumptions. It must be remembered, however, that once the correct kind of time-temperature behaviour has been built into the theory by assuming molecular rupture to be an activated process, the use of a few fitting constants is sufficient to give reasonable agreement with fact even though the basic mechanism may be at fault. The simple approach of Greensmith thus appears most promising since it has a sound empirical basis. Visco-elasticity theory can then be used to show that the empirical relationship between propagation rate, stress and temperature, used in this theory, can be predicted from molecular concepts.

5.5 FATIGUE FRACTURE

Although there may or may not be an initial induction period during which fatigue cracks are initiated under cyclic deformation, fatigue fracture eventually occurs by the incremental growth of cracks. Fatigue thus presupposes non-catastrophic propagation of fracture since the crack *must* grow each cycle but only by a small amount insufficient to cause macroscopic failure of the material. The phenomenon cannot therefore be explained as an initiation process, nor even as a propagation process in which crack stability is the result of purely geometrical factors as in section 5.1, but must involve intrinsically stable propagation.

In metals this stability is the result of plastic flow, the fatigue crack being supposed to originate and grow by the movement of dislocations to the tip. In polymeric solids the stabilising factors may be the dependence of $\mathscr{T}$ upon rate of propagation, according to which acceleration of the crack is discouraged, or it may be the stationary stress-distribution mechanism discussed above. The first of these factors may result from plasticity or visco-elasticity and the second from non-visco-elastic hysteresis.

We assume initially that fatigue fracture commences at the intrinsic flaws already discussed in Chapter 4.2 which may be regarded as pre-existing cracks of length c_0. We shall defer till later the question of flaw generation in fatigue. In elastomers, where the most thorough study of fatigue has so far been carried out, there is evidence that ozone cracks (see Chapter 5.6) are often responsible for the initiation of the process. There are two types of fatigue fracture to be considered depending whether the incremental growth in a single cycle is time dependent or not.

(i) *Rate-independent fatigue*

Let us consider first the case of time-independent growth such as found in crystallising rubbers where stationary stress-distributions are encountered. The small-scale growth which occurs during a single application of load to the specimen was given earlier for natural rubber as,

$$\Delta c \simeq p(\partial\mathscr{E}/\partial A)_1^2 \tag{5.3}$$

$$-(\partial\mathscr{E}/\partial A)_1 < \mathscr{T} \text{('slip')}.$$

Upon relaxation of the specimen the crack is found to regain its original condition and a further application of load produces a further increment of growth in accordance with equation (5.3). This is because the strain induced crystallisation which is responsible for the stationary distribution phenomenon disappears completely at zero stress. Writing, from equation (4.22)

$$-(\partial \mathscr{E}/\partial A)_1 = -(1/2h)(\partial \mathscr{E}/\partial c)_1 = KcW$$

we find that an internal crack of length c lying perpendicular to the external stress direction will propagate a distance,

$$\Delta c = pK^2c^2W^2 \tag{5.29}$$

during each cycle. A fatigue crack of original length c_0 will grow to a length c in a number of cycles N given by

$$\frac{dc}{dN} = pK^2c^2W^2$$

and, integrating

$$\int_{c_0}^{c} \frac{dc}{c^2} = pK^2W^2 \int_{0}^{N} dN$$

$$\left(\frac{1}{c_0} - \frac{1}{c}\right) = pK^2W^2N. \tag{5.30}$$

If c, the final length of the crack, is now put equal to infinity, N is the number of cycles to failure and is given by,

$$N_f = (pK^2W^2c_0)^{-1}. \tag{5.31}$$

The constants p and K can be obtained from model experiments in which c_0 is a relatively large crack introduced intentionally or alternatively from cyclic crack propagation results obtained on one of the test pieces described in Chapter 4. The value of c_0 may thus be predicted from N_f the number of cycles to failure and the dependence of N on W, and the independence of c_0 and W, may be checked experimentally.[37] Fig. 5.22(a) shows the dependence of crack length c upon the number of cycles N in a single experiment and confirms equation (5.30). Using the slope of this line and the value of N required for an un-notched specimen, the natural flaw size c_0 is predicted to be about 10^{-3} cm, a value consistent with the known nature of the specimen surfaces. Fig. 5.22(b) which shows data for natural rubber fatigued under different maximum stresses confirms that N_f is proportional to W^{-2} as predicted by the theory.

12

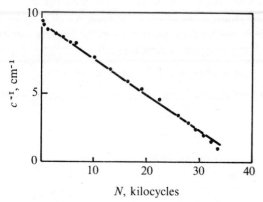

FIG. 5.22(a)   Growth of a fatigue crack in natural rubber
(after Greensmith, Mullins and Thomas[37]).

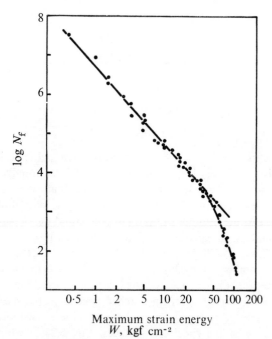

FIG. 5.22(b) Dependence of fatigue life upon stored
energy density in natural rubber (after Greensmith,
and Mullins Thomas[37]).

(ii) Rate-dependent fatigue

In materials not subject to stationary-stress distributions, the growth in a given cycle will be both a function of $(\partial \mathscr{E}/\partial A)_1$ and of time t. As previously discussed the rate of propagation of extensive cracks is constant at a given value of $(\partial \mathscr{E}/\partial A)_1$ so that from equation (5.12) we may write, for an increment of fatigue growth,

$$\frac{dc}{dN} = \int_0^t \frac{dc}{dt} dt = q \int_0^t (-\partial \mathscr{E}/\partial A)_1^n dt$$

where t is the time required for a single cycle and n is some power to be determined. For simplicity we assume that the specimen is loaded and unloaded instantaneously and that, whilst loaded $(\partial \mathscr{E}/\partial A)_1$ is held constant. Then

$$dc/dN = q(-\partial \mathscr{E}/\partial A)_1^n t$$
$$= q K^n c^n W^n t$$

whence, integrating as before we obtain,

$$\frac{1}{n-1}\left(\frac{1}{c_0^{n-1}} - \frac{1}{c^{n-1}}\right) = q K^n W^n t N \tag{5.32}$$

or letting $c \to \infty$ and rearranging,

$$N_f = (n-1)^{-1}(q K^n W^n t c_0^{n-1})^{-1} \tag{5.33}$$

where N_f is now the number of cycles to failure. As in the case of time-independent fatigue, experiment confirms the form of dependence of N_f upon W, the exponent n turning out to be approximately 4 for SBR gum rubber as opposed to 2 for gum natural rubber. (The addition of carbon filler to these rubbers affects the values of p and q but not of n.) The dependence of N_f upon cycling rate, and therefore upon t, has not been so thoroughly checked but under isothermal conditions N_f certainly increases as the frequency of cycling is raised as predicted by equation 5.33.

As might be expected, the temperature of test also has a profound effect upon the rate of fatigue in non-crystallising elastomers, the contrast between natural rubber and SBR in this respect being indicated in Fig. 5.23. The behaviour of the SBR can be covered by the mathematical treatment by allowing the 'constant' q to vary with temperature in accordance with the data of Fig. 5.5 which relates $(\partial c/\partial t)$ to $(\partial \mathscr{E}/\partial A)_1$.

(iii) *Fatigue stress limit*

The foregoing discussion of fatigue crack propagation assumes that flaws exist for which $-(\partial \mathscr{E}/\partial A)_l$ exceeds $\mathscr{T}$ at the stress level obtaining in the specimen. Since, however, $-(\partial \mathscr{E}/\partial A)_l = KcW$ and provided the pre-existent flaw size c_0 does not exceed some given value, it follows that there will be some value of the stored energy density,

$$W_0 \sim \mathscr{T}/Kc_0$$

below which no fatigue growth can take place. Taking values of $c_0 = 10^{-3}$ cm and $\mathscr{T} = 10^4$ to 10^6 erg cm^{-2} we obtain (with $K = \pi$)

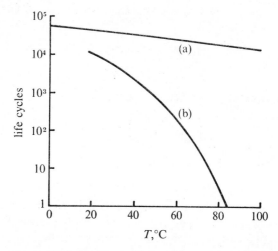

FIG. 5.23   Dependence of fatigue life upon temperature in gum vulcanisates of (a) natural rubber and (b) SBR. Strain cycle 0·175%, frequency 100 cpm (after Greensmith, Mullins and Thomas[37]).

values for the limiting stored energy density in the region of 10^6 to 10^8 erg cm^{-3}. This compares with an observed value in SBR rubber of about 10^6 erg cm^{-3}. A similar calculation for PMMA, using $\mathscr{T} = 3 \times 10^5$ erg cm^{-2} and $c_0 = 10^{-2}$ cm gives a critical value for W_0 of 5×10^6 erg cm^{-3}. Taking Young's Modulus for the methacrylate as 3×10^3 kgf cm^{-2} this predicts a fatigue limit stress of 170 kgf cm^{-2} which compares well with the fatigue limit of 150 to 300 kgf cm^{-2} obtained by Zarek [38] for PMMA.

(iv) *Generation of flaws*

So far in this discussion it has been assumed that the fatigue process can be regarded simply as the incremental growth of pre-existent flaws and this has been shown sufficient to explain major features of fatigue in polymers such as the existence of a fatigue limit and a linear dependence of the logarithm of the number of cycles to failure upon the stored energy density in the specimen. On the other hand it is recognised that these initial flaws are often the result of other fracture processes such as ozone cracking or the stress crazing which creates intrinsic flaws of the order of 0·1 to 0·5 mm in PMMA (see Chapter 4.2), so that it is not beyond possibility that in some materials cyclic loading itself may generate a further class of intrinsic flaw. This process of fatigue crack *initiation* would be superimposed upon the propagation process detailed above and might contribute significantly to the number of cycles N required to cause fatigue fracture. This may be represented as follows,

$$N_t(\text{total}) = N_i(\text{initiation}) + N_p(\text{propagation})$$

where so far we have considered only N_p. There is at present little experimental evidence that N_i is significant but the theory of Prevorsek and Lyons [39] for fatigue fracture in polymer fibres suggests that in these materials $N_t \sim N_i$ and that propagation plays relatively little part in the process. The theory adopts the statistical approach of Chapter 4 to calculate the growth of flaws under conditions where the maximum value of $-(\partial \mathscr{E}/\partial A)_l$ in a cycle is less than the critical value $\mathscr{T}$ for mechanical propagation. As is to be anticipated the theory predicts a similar inter-relation between stress, time (frequency of cycling) and temperature as is found for creep fracture and such dependence has been observed in the cyclic fatigue of polymers. However it must be realised that this inter-relation (e.g., the equivalence of a temperature shift to a change in the logarithm of the frequency) will appear whenever activated processes are encountered and will not distinguish between one such mechanism and another. Thus the dependence of $\mathscr{T}$ upon temperature and rate in a viscoelastic material would produce the same kind of experimental data as predicted by a statistical growth theory, although the two mechanisms are quite distinct.

(v) *Behaviour of the crack tip during fatigue*

Detailed study of the crack during the fatigue process reveals that the actual mechanisms involved are by no means simple. We have already seen that in reinforced elastomers the crack deviates from its axis during a single extension of the test piece and it is found in some cases (specially the strain-crystallising rubbers) that relaxation restores the *status quo* so that the next increment of growth reproduces the first and so on. This process generates a cusped profile on the surface of fracture and the incremental nature of fatigue is thus made visible under the microscope (Fig. 5.24). Frequently the fracture surface is marked by steps or level differences indicating that fracture is proceeding in several different though parallel planes and at these steps the incremental growth is diminished (Fig. 5.25). In severe cases, i.e., very many steps, the surface may become so rough that it is difficult to pick out the growth lines which are so easily visible under 'smooth' conditions. In elastomers rough growth is the condition usually encountered and much care has to be taken to preserve smooth growth in experimental studies. This, of course, is a good thing from a practical viewpoint since under rough growth conditions p in equation (5.3) assumes a value ten or even a hundred times smaller than for smooth growth, thus increasing the fatigue life proportionately. From a theoretical viewpoint, however, variations in p with roughness make it more difficult to study the fatigue process quantitatively as can be done for smooth fatigue cracks.

It is perhaps this difficulty of establishing stable smooth fatigue cracks that has so far hindered the application of the present theory to materials other than elastomers. The incremental growth of cracks has, however, been observed in PMMA and polyethylene and quantitative data may soon be available for these and other plastic materials. It is likely that fatigue in *crystalline* polymers may present phenomena not encountered in the simple fatigue of elastomers. This is indicated by the behaviour of natural rubber when the fatigue cycle is not allowed to pass through zero strain. Under these conditions the strain-crystallised material at the tip of the crack never melts and the growth per cycle is drastically reduced. It is also found that a relatively large advance of the crack may occur suddenly, after many cycles with no apparent growth. Some further details of fatigue crack surfaces in natural rubber are given in Chapter 6 where fracture surfaces are discussed.

5.6 STRESS-CORROSION CRACKING IN POLYMERS

The phenomenon of cracking under stress in a corrosive environment was described in Chapter 3. The discussion here concerns the

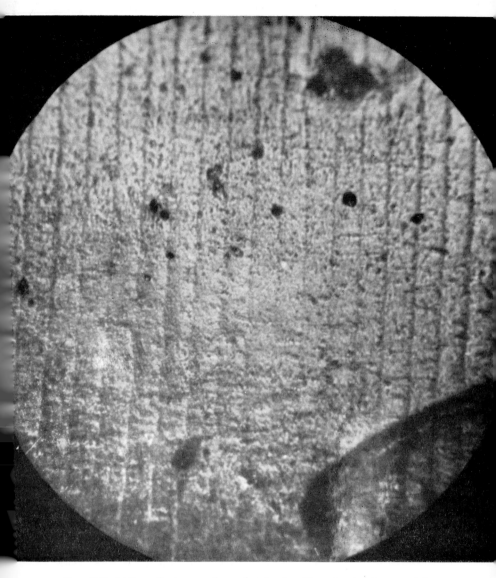

FIG. 5.24 Fatigue fracture surface of natural rubber showing incremental growth. Fracture direction is horizontal. Magnification 975.

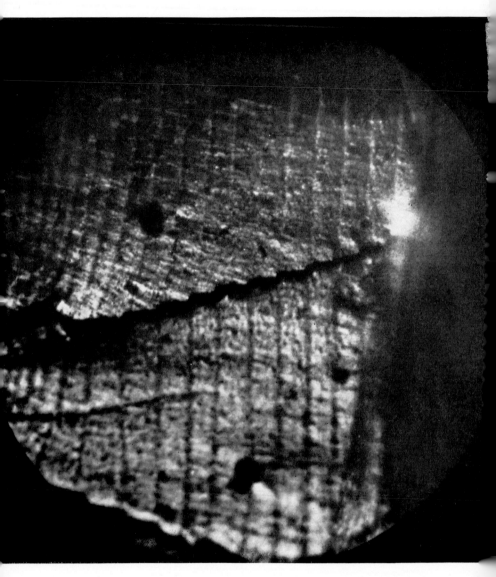

FIG. 5.25   As Fig. 5.24 but containing a 'roughness' step at which crack growth has been retarded. Magnification 975.

application of our fracture theory to this process. As in the case of fatigue fracture, most of the definitive work on the mechanics of corrosion cracking has so far been carried out on rubber, i.e., in connection with the phenomenon of ozone cracking, but there is now experimental evidence that the same principles apply to brittle polymers exposed to solvents and will no doubt be found valuable in studying the phenomenon in general.

(i) Critical energy for ozone cracking

Braden and Gent [40] studied the propagation of a single preformed crack in a strip of rubber exposed, under stress, to known concentrations of ozone (Fig. 5.26). The specimen's major surfaces were protected from ozone by a layer of silicone grease thus ensuring that

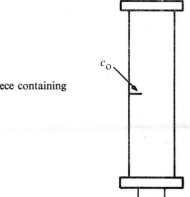

FIG. 5.26   Ozone cracking test-piece containing edge crack.

attack occurred only at the crack tip itself. The rate of propagation r was measured by microscope as a function of the load on the test piece, the crack depth and the ozone concentration. Up to a certain critical load no propagation was observed but once this load had been exceeded the crack grew at a rate independent of load. By changing the depth c_0 of the initial crack (made with a razor blade) and by using rubbers of different elastic moduli it was soon shown that propagation commenced not at a critical load but rather at a critical value of the parameter $-(\partial \mathscr{E}/\partial A)_l$ which equals Kc_0W for the test piece in Fig. 5.26. Fig. 5.27 shows the dependence of the critical value of W upon c_0^{-1} for specimens of natural rubber, establishing the constancy of $c_0 W$ at the onset of propagation. The discovery that the same basic principles of fracture propagation apply to phenomena as diverse as ozone cracking and direct fracture is gratifying and important.

The critical value of $-(\partial \mathscr{E}/\partial A)_l$ for ozone cracking will be denoted $\mathscr{T}_0$ by analogy with the corresponding quantity $\mathscr{T}$ referring to mechanical propagation. One important difference between $\mathscr{T}_0$ and

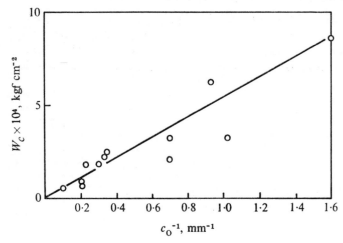

FIG. 5.27   Dependence of critical energy-density for ozone cracking upon crack length (after Braden and Gent[40]).

$\mathscr{T}$ emerges immediately in that the ozone cracking parameter is very much the smaller. In fact $\mathscr{T}_0$ has a characteristic value which varies little from one polymer to another and is about 100 erg cm^{-2}, i.e., of the correct order for a true surface energy. This contrasts with values of up to 10^7 erg cm^{-2} for mechanical fracture and it is evident that in ozone cracking very little energy is dissipated in plastic or visco-elastic deformations at the propagating crack. In mechanical fracture it is necessary to generate sufficiently high stresses at the crack tip to break chemical bonds of one sort or another and irreversible deformations in the vicinity of the crack tip are unavoidable. In ozone cracking, however, the chemical bonds are broken by chemical reaction so that very high stresses at the tip are unnecessary (the strain at the tip of an ozone crack has been estimated to be some 30 per cent compared with perhaps 700 per cent for mechanical fracture). Under these circumstances then it appears that the Griffith criterion is adequate to account for the whole process and the only energy supplied to the crack is that necessary to provide for the fresh surfaces created by propagation.

So far we have considered the propagation of a pre-existing crack, but just as the results of Berry for brittle fracture in PMMA and polystyrene could be extrapolated to account for behaviour in specimens containing only intrinsic flaws, so may present data since,

$$\mathcal{T}_0 = Kc_0(\text{artificial})W_1 = Kc_0(\text{intrinsic})W_2$$

where W_1 and W_2 are the stored energy densities required to produce critical ozone cracking in the notched and un-notched specimens respectively. A value of 10^{-3} cm is predicted for the intrinsic flaw size in elastomers from this calculation and the intrinsic flaws are thus seen to be of a similar nature to those responsible for initiating mechanical fracture.

FIG. 5.28   Penetration of an ozone crack into an elastomeric surface. Shaded region represents degraded layer thinning to a minimum at the root of the crack.

Electron microscopy [41] has cast further light on the origin of ozone cracks and the critical energy condition for their propagation. In surfaces where the strain energy density is less than that required to produce ozone cracks from the intrinsic flaws present, replicas show that ozone attack produces degradation of a surface layer. This layer increases in thickness in proportion to the square root of the time of exposure and the process is so slow that no macroscopically observable changes occur. This is because the ozone must diffuse through an increasingly thick layer of degraded rubber, having an oily consistency, before it can react with the unreacted rubber which lies beneath. When however the energy necessary to create fresh surfaces is available to a flaw, etch pits appear in the surface under attack and develop into running cracks which penetrate into the surface rapidly since they provide immediate access of ozone molecules to the underlying unreacted rubber (Fig. 5.28). The parameter

$\mathcal{T}_0$ therefore represents the surface energy of the degraded rubber plus any energy absorbed viscously in separating the molecules of this material. This picture is strengthened by the discovery [42,43] that certain chemical additives, which prevent ozonolytic degradation of the rubber and produce a coherent layer on the surface of the specimen when the latter is exposed to ozone, cause a dramatic increase in the value of $\mathcal{T}_0$. The microscopy of ozone attack in elastomers is further discussed in Chapter 6.

(ii) *Rate of ozone crack propagation*

The rate of ozone crack propagation is independent of the forces on the specimen provided $-(\partial\mathcal{E}/\partial A)_l > \mathcal{T}_0$. This is true as long as ozone attack occurs only at the crack tip itself and not in the strained area around the tip as, for example, on the major surfaces of a sheet containing an edge crack. Under these circumstances the time to failure of a stressed specimen must depend only upon the dimensions of the specimen. The rate of growth is however directly proportional to the ozone concentration, underlining the fact that a molecule at the crack tip can only allow passage of the fracture front after it has been broken by reaction with one or more molecules of ozone. The rate is also a function of temperature, but here an interesting point emerges.

TABLE 5.2

(Ozone concentration 1·15 mg O_3 per litre)

Polymer	Rate of crack growth (mm min⁻¹)		
	2°C	20°C	50°C
NR	0·15	0·22	0·19
SBR	0·13	0·37	0·34
Butyl rubber	0·00	0·02	0·16
60/40 Butadiene-acrylonitrile	0·004	0·04	0·23

In rubbers having relatively little mechanical hysteresis at low strains, such as natural rubber and SBR, the rate of propagation is not greatly affected by temperature over the range 0 to 50°C. Rubbers which have relatively high mechanical hysteresis in this temperature range, such as butyl rubber, demonstrate a dramatic increase in the propagation rate as the temperature rises. The data are given in Table 5.2.[40]

At 0°C both the butyl and the butadiene-acrylonitrile rubbers are highly hysteresial because close to their glass transition temperatures. As the temperature rises a rapid increase occurs in molecular mobility, whereas both NR and SBR, having transition temperatures about -70 to $-80°C$, have high molecular mobility throughout the temperature range 0 to 50°C. This suggests that the propagation rate is directly related to the mobility of the polymer molecules and, by inference, to the rate of diffusion of the ozone into the polymer at the tip of the crack. This is borne out also by the observation that plasticisation of butyl rubber at 20°C also increases propagation rates from 0·02 to 0·24 mm min^{-1} whilst NR and SBR remain unaffected by similar treatment.

(iii) *Corrosion cracking in plastics*

As outlined in Chapter 3 most investigations of stress corrosion cracking in plastics have considered the cumulative effect of many flaws and only the time-to-break has been used to characterise the process. We shall return presently to the question of breaking time, but before doing so mention will be made of recent experiments on PMMA analogous to those discussed above for elastomers. Sheets of PMMA about 10 cm wide and containing a preformed edge crack were loaded in tension using a cantilever device and immersed in various solvents known to cause stress cracking in this material. Progress of the crack was observed by travelling microscope and just as in the case of the elastomers a critical value of the stored energy density W, was found to be necessary to cause crack propagation. As before also the product Wc_0 was constant at the onset of cracking for cracks of different original lengths, c_0, so that a critical energy criterion appears to operate in PMMA also. The critical energy $\mathscr{T}$ turns out to be of the order of 4000 erg cm^{-2} for cracking of PMMA in methylated spirits at 25°C but is lower for benzene and higher for petroleum ether. This value for $\mathscr{T}$ is much higher than a true surface energy but much lower than for mechanical crack propagation where values of 10^5 erg cm^{-2} obtain.

When the cracking medium is methylated spirits the preformed crack (which is actually a natural crack produced by driving a wedge into an initial sawcut) advances slowly and uniformly without any geometrical change, but in a more active solvent like benzene subsidiary cracks appear in the major surfaces of the sheet in the highly stressed region around the crack tip causing an increase in the apparent propagation rate by joining up with the primary crack. The same phenomenon was found in the ozone cracking of elastomers when the major surfaces of the sheets were not protected by grease. This multiple crazing gives rise to a dependence of overall cracking rate (and thus of the time-to-break) upon load whereas the ideal propagation of a single crack, in some cases at least, is diffusion controlled and independent of stress.

(iv) *Time-to-break in corrosion stress cracking*

In spite of the evidence adduced above that the basic mechanism of corrosion cracking involves crack propagation at a velocity governed by diffusion rather than stress, the facts of the matter are that the overall time-to-break of a specimen is dependent upon the stress level in the specimen. It was suggested above that this may be the result of multiple cracking and the consequences of such a theory may be quite simply deduced.

It has been shown that in rubbers undergoing ozone cracking a vast number of sub-microscopic cracks are initiated but that most of these fail to propagate because the stress field around them is relieved by the presence of nearby cracks. Braden and Gent [40] have shown that the number of cracks which actually survive must be proportional to the stored energy density W in the test piece. If we now suppose that separate cracks link up to cause ultimate failure of the specimen we would expect fracture to occur in a time inversely proportional to the number of available cracks, i.e., to the stored energy density

$$t_f = \alpha W^{-1}. \tag{5.34}$$

If the stress on the specimen is considered this becomes for a Hookean material

$$t_f = \beta \sigma_f^{-2}$$
$$\log t_f = \log \beta - 2 \log \sigma_f \tag{5.35}$$

α and β being constants. A plot of $\log t_f$ against $\log \sigma_f$ should therefore have a slope of -2 and this is in fact the case for some data given by Gaube [44] for high density polyethylene immersed in water (Fig. 3.11). The slope -2 is, of course, only found for stresses below the yield stress of the material since it is only here that the elastic analysis of Braden and Gent applies.

A more elaborate theory to account for the dependence of time-to-break upon stress level in polyethylene has been propounded by

Tung [45] who considered that a local critical strain was necessary to initiate cracking and that the rate of attainment of this critical strain must be dependent upon stress because of the visco-elastic nature of the material. The theory is not highly successful in predicting time-to-fracture but Tung's work underlines the importance of visco-elasticity in the phenomenon of corrosion stress cracking. In order to take this into account in the simple multiple-crack theory outlined above allowance would have to be made for the variation of elastic modulus (and thus of W at a given stress) with time.

A further possibility is that a single crack may propagate at a rate governed by the overall stress because higher stress facilitates access of the corrosive fluid by opening the crack to a greater extent. Such an effect would obviously not be noticed in ozone cracking of rubber since the high deformability of the latter ensures free access to the crack tip at the lowest stress levels. Further study of these problems should enable us to answer the outstanding questions relating to the mechanism of stress-corrosion cracking.

References

1. ROESLER, F. C. *Proc. Phys. Soc., B*, **69,** 981 (1956).
2. HERTZ, H. *Collected Works*, Barth (Leipzig), vol. 1, 174 (1895).
3. BENBOW, J. J., and ROESLER, F. C. *Proc. Phys. Soc., B*, **70,** 201 (1957).
4. BERRY, J. P. *J. appl. Phys.*, **34,** 62 (1963).
5. SVENNSON, N. L. *Proc. Phys. Soc.*, **77,** 876 (1961).
6. BROUTMAN, L. J., and MCGARRY, F. J. *J. appl. Polym. Sci.*, **9,** 589 (1965).
7. BERRY, J. P. *Nature*, **185,** 91 (1960).
8. BROUTMAN, L. J., and MCGARRY, F. J. *J. appl. Polym. Sci.*, **9,** 609 (1965).
9. THOMAS, A. G. *J. appl. Polym. Sci.*, **3,** 171 (1960).
10. GREENSMITH, H. W., and THOMAS, A. G. *J. Polym. Sci.*, **18,** 189 (1955).
11. MULLINS, L. *Trans. I.R.I.*, **35,** 213 (1959).
12. GREENSMITH, H. W. *J. Polym. Sci.*, **21,** 175 (1956).
13. THOMAS, A. G. *J. Polym. Sci.*, **31,** 467 (1958).
14. ANDREWS, E. H. *J. appl. Phys.*, **32,** 542 (1961).
15. INGLIS, C. E. *Trans. Inst. Naval Architects, Lond.*, **60,** 219 (1913).
16. TIMOSHENKO, S. P., and GOODIER, J. N. *Theory of Elasticity*, 2nd ed., McGraw-Hill (1951).

17. DONNELL, L. H. *California Inst. Tech.*, *T. von Kármán Anniv. Vol.* p. 293 (1941).
18. MUSKHELISVILI, N. I. *Some basic Problems of the Mathematical Theory of Elasticity*, P. Noordhoff Ltd., Groningen (1953).
19. NEUBER, H. *Theory of Notch Stresses*, Springer-Verlag, Berlin (1958).
20. WESTERGAARD, H. M. *J. appl. Mech.*, **6** (2), A–49 (1939).
21. SNEDDON, I. N. *Proc. R. Soc.*, *A*, **187**, 229 (1946).
22. ELLIOTT, H. A. *Proc. Phys. Soc.*, **59**, 208 (1947).
23. IRWIN, G. R. *J. appl. Mech.*, **24**, 361 (1957).
24. *Special ASTM Bulletin Report on Fracture Testing of High Strength Sheet Materials* 29 (Jan. 1960).
25. COOK, J., and GORDON, J. E. *Proc. R. Soc.*, *A*, **282**, 508 (1964).
26. IRWIN, G. R. *J. bas. Engng*, **82**, 417 (June 1960).
27. ANDREWS, E. H. *Proc. Phys. Soc.*, **77**, 483 (1961).
28. ANDREWS, E. H. *J. Mech. Phys. Solids*, **11**, 231 (1963).
29. YOFFE, E. H. *Phil. Mag.* **42**, 739 (1951).
30. GREENSMITH, H. W. *J. appl. Polym. Sci.*, **8**, 1113 (1964).
31. ROSEN, B. (Ed.). *Fracture Processes in Polymeric Solids*, p. 429, John Wiley and Sons, Inc. (1964).
32. TAYLOR, G. R., and DARIN, S. R. *J. Polym. Sci.*, **17**, 511 (1955).
33. BUECHE, A. M. *J. Polym. Sci.*, **19**, 275 (1956).
34. BUECHE, F. *J. appl. Phys.*, **26**, 1133 (1955). *J. Polym. Sci.*, **24**, 189 (1957). BUECHE, F., and T. DUDEK, *Rubber Chem. Technol.*, **36**, 1 (1963).
35. HALPIN, J. C. *J. appl. Phys.*, **35**, 3133 (1964).
36. KNAUSS, W. G. Ph.D. Thesis, California Inst. of Technol., Pasadena, California (1963).
37. GREENSMITH, H. W., *et al.*, *Chemistry and Physics of Rubberlike Substances* (ed. L. Bateman), p. 291, Maclaren and Sons Ltd. (1963).
38. ZAREK, J. M. *Br. Plast.* **30**, 399 (1957).
39. PREVORSEK, D., and LYONS, W. J. *J. appl. Phys.*, **35**, 3152 (1964).
40. BRADEN, M., and GENT, A. N. *J. appl. Polym. Sci.*, **3**, 90 (1960).
41. ANDREWS, E. H., and BRADEN, M. *J. Polym. Sci.*, **55**, 787 (1961).
42. BRADEN, M., and GENT, A. N. *J. appl. Polym. Sci.*, **6**, 449 (1962).
43. ANDREWS, E. H., and BRADEN, M. *J. appl. Polym. Sci.*, **1**, 1003 (1963).
44. GAUBE, E. *Kunstoffe*, **49**, 446 (1959).
45. TUNG, L. H. *J. Polym. Sci.*, *A*, **3**, 1045 (1965).

CHAPTER 6

Fracture Surfaces

The examination of fracture surfaces ('fractography') has been used widely in the study of metals and glass. It is generally possible to tell from the appearance of the surfaces where fracture has originated, in which direction it has travelled and what has been its general nature (e.g., ductile or brittle). More detailed study may also provide information about the velocity of fracture and the incidence of subsidiary or secondary fractures. The fracture surfaces of polymeric materials yield similar data and their study is of great practical importance as well as scientific interest. On the other hand, great care must be exercised in interpreting fracture markings (i.e., the features observed on the surface of fracture) since confusion can easily occur and instances of this will be given in the course of this chapter.

What general kinds of information can we expect to glean from a study of fracture surfaces? If the fracture took the form of a perfect plane through the solid we should, of course, see nothing; the incidence of fracture markings betrays deviation of the fracture from the planar form expected from basic considerations such as Griffith's theory. What may cause such deviations? The most obvious cause is inhomogeneity in the material concerned. Any obstacle to the fracture will turn the latter aside whilst any point of weakness in the material will tend to 'attract' the fracture through itself. An obvious example is that of a polymer containing a hard filler such as carbon black. In such a material the fracture front does not cleave the particles in its path but passes around them leaving a bump in one fracture surface and a depression in the other.[1] We see then that the first kind of information provided by a fracture surface relates to the structure of the material itself. Not only does the structure affect the path taken by the fracture but conversely the fracture path reveals the microstructure of the material. Fracture can therefore be a tool for the study of microstructures and has indeed been used to reveal such things as filler structures, phase separation and crystalline morphology in polymers.

It does not follow, however, that a fracture surface in an inhomogeneous material provides an exact 'photograph' of the structure, as will be seen presently. Even in the simple case of spherical filler particles the *quantity* of filler seen is in excess of that expected from the known loading of the material [1] and in other cases interpretation is even more difficult. The reason why the fracture surface does not precisely represent the structure is clear; there are fracture markings which arise from the behaviour of the fracture itself apart from or in addition to the presence of structure in the material. In what follows, therefore, we shall consider fracture markings under three headings. Firstly those that reveal in a fairly faithful manner the microstructure of the solid. Secondly those that involve both structure and the behaviour of the fracture front and thirdly those that arise purely from the latter behaviour and which may therefore be observed in completely homogeneous materials. This last heading will also include effects caused by the deformation behaviour of the material, i.e., by its plasticity or visco-elasticity.

6.1 *Microstructural Observations in Fracture Surfaces*

The internal microstructure of a material can be studied visually in one of three ways. A thin section can be cut from the solid and viewed in transmission under either a light or an electron microscope. Alternatively the material may be cut to expose a surface which is then etched to reveal detail whilst a third method, and that which concerns us here, is to fracture the material and study the resulting surfaces. It is, of course, only effective where plastic flow is negligible.

The method usually employed for the study of fracture surfaces is to make a replica of the surface which is sufficiently thin to permit the use of transmission microscopy. This is almost essential if electron microscopy is contemplated since reflection techniques give low resolution, involve serious foreshortening of the image and are difficult to use on poorly conducting specimens. These comments do not apply to the recently developed scanning electron microscope which promises to be of immense value in the direct observation of surfaces. Resolution is still limited, however, to about 100Å. If the optical microscope is to be used, of course, reflection methods may be applied directly to the specimen, but even here replicas may prove advantageous, giving better definition of the actual surface.

The replication of polymeric materials is usually carried out using a two-stage technique. A fairly concentrated solution of some film-forming material, such as 'formvar', polystyrene or gelatine is first applied to the surface to be studied and allowed to set. Gelatine or some other water-soluble material is to be preferred for replicating polymers because organic solvents may swell and so deform the surface to be studied. When the first-stage replica has set it is stripped off and coated with a thin layer of evaporated carbon or silica as

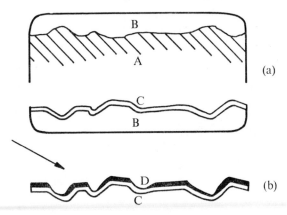

FIG. 6.1 Replication process. (A) polymer surface, (B) first stage replica, (C) evaporated carbon film, (D) evaporated metal shadowing.

indicated in Fig. 6.1(a). This evaporated layer constitutes the second-stage or final replica and for electron microscopy is made some 500 Å thick. It is generally necessary to 'shadow' such a replica by evaporating a small quantity of heavy metal on to it at an angle (Fig. 6.1(b)) to show up the surface relief. The topography of such replicas may be further revealed by the use of stereoscopic methods which are particularly effective with the electron microscope.

Quantitatively, replica methods are of little use since the fracture surface is not a random plane through the material as is a sectioned or polished surface and it is therefore impossible to use a fracture surface to find out, e.g., how *much* of a second phase is present in the solid. This is well illustrated by measurements of the quantity of carbon filler observed in electron micrographs of fracture surfaces

13

of filled rubbers (Fig. 3.16). The carbon black particles appear either in silhouette (where they have been extracted from the surface by the replica) or else as pits and bumps in the surface. If the fracture were

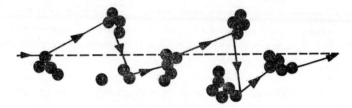

FIG. 6.2   Fracture path in a carbon-filled rubber. Broken line represents ideal or random plane behaviour.

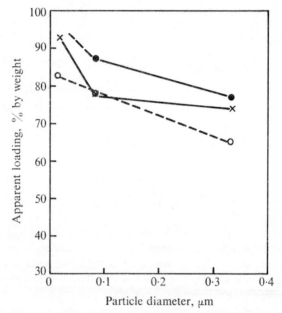

FIG. 6.3   Apparent loading in some carbon-filled SBR rubbers as deduced from replicas of fracture surfaces. True loading in all cases is 30% (after Andrews and Walsh[1]).

a random plane through the material, the area occupied in the picture by filler should correspond to the volume proportion of filler in the material, but in fact the apparent loading is always greater than the actual by a factor of two or more because the fracture has travelled

FIG. 6.4   Fracture surface of a natural rubber—PMMA blend showing spherical PMMA phase particles. Magnification 40 000.

preferentially from one particle or aggregate of particles to the next (Fig. 6.2). Some actual figures [1] for apparent loading are given in Fig. 6.3.

In spite of this quantitative failure the fractographic study of micro-structures has some advantages. It is very much simpler in some materials than sectioning or etching and it does give some striking results that might not be obtainable by other methods. A fracture is the finest of 'knives' cutting cleanly around features as small as 30 Å in size and revealing them plainly in the microscope.

The method of replicating fracture surfaces has been used to study the microstructure of polymer blends. Fig. 6.21 shows a blend of natural rubber and ethylene-propylene rubber in which complete phase separation has occurred,[2] and Fig. 6.4. a blend of natural rubber with PMMA. In the latter system it was found possible to define the locus of polymerisation of methyl methacrylate monomer in natural rubber latex by the study of fracture surfaces.[3] The methacrylate monomer was mixed into the latex and a polymerisation catalyst added. The final polymer blend was dried to a solid form and fractured for examination. When the catalyst used was oil-soluble, i.e., capable of penetrating the rubber latex particles, the methacrylate was found to polymerise in the form of small globules within the larger rubber latex particles. If the catalyst were a water-soluble material, having access only to the latex particle surfaces, polymerisation occurred on those surfaces which were found to be encrusted with the PMMA globules. In the latter cases the PMMA formed a continuous network throughout the final blend which was thus relatively hard and leathery whilst in the case of an oil soluble catalyst the PMMA particles were well dispersed in an elastomer matrix and the blend was consequently rubbery. This example shows how useful fractography can be in following the locus of chemical reactions in polymeric solids.

A further fruitful application of replica methods has been in the study of crystalline texture in semi-crystalline polymers. Much of the information on this subject discussed in Chapter 1 has been obtained by cooling the material to liquid nitrogen temperatures and fracturing it to reveal internal structure.[4] In some cases lamellae are actually extracted from the polymer and, adhering to the replica, may be studied in the electron microscope.

In certain instances it is possible to reveal not only the micro-structure itself but something of its response to the high local stresses developed during fracture. The case of carbon black filler in rubber can again be used to illustrate this. Some of the particles exposed in the fracture surface are actually loose, the bond between the particle and the rubber having been broken down completely under high stress, and these particles are removed from the surface by replication and may thus be counted. The amount of breakdown varies markedly with the type of filler and the type of rubber as well as with the

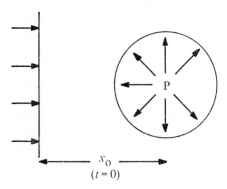

FIG. 6.5 Interaction between primary and secondary fractures.

chemistry of the vulcanising system so that the fracture surface provides information about the strength of the filler-to-rubber bond in the material. In a given vulcanisate the extraction is, furthermore, dependent upon the nature of the fracture itself. In brittle fracture at liquid nitrogen temperatures very little filler is extracted, and this reflects the narrowness of the crack and the consequently limited volume under high stress at its tip. In room temperature fracture, where very high strains are developed at the tip, the amount of filler-rubber breakdown is large, though even here the quantity is dependent upon the speed of fracture.[1]

6.2 FRACTURE MARKINGS INVOLVING MICROSTRUCTURE AND THE BEHAVIOUR OF THE FRACTURE ITSELF

(i) Conic markings

Many interesting fracture markings arise when the fracture front is deviated from its normal planar path as an indirect result of the presence of microstructural features. Perhaps the most common and the most striking are markings caused by the incidence of secondary fracture, a phenomenon already discussed briefly in Chapter 3 in connection with energy losses during fracture propagation. The stress concentrations at inhomogeneities in the body, when super-imposed on that surrounding the approaching front, cause the breaking stress of the material to be exceeded in a number of dis-persed regions in front of and to either side of the main fracture. These secondary fractures spread in a circular manner in a plane parallel to the main fracture and if this plane is sufficiently close to that of the latter the two may become joined by a small step in the surface, the main fracture being diverted into the secondary fracture plane.[5] Suppose the main fracture is a straight edge advancing from left to right in the $x-y$ plane (Fig. 6.5) at a velocity v and that a secondary fracture is initiated at a point P (in a parallel plane a small distance Δz away) when the main fracture is a distance x_0 away (time $t = 0$). If the secondary fracture expands in a circular fashion at a radial velocity u the two fracture fronts will 'intersect' along a small step of height Δz having a locus in the $x-y$ plane given by,

$$x = vt$$
$$y = \{u^2t^2-(x_0-x)^2\}^{\frac{1}{2}}$$

which reduces to

$$x^2((u^2/v^2)-1)-y^2 = x_0(x_0-2x).$$

This equation bears a strong resemblance to a conic, becoming quasi-parabolic if $u = v$ and otherwise resembling either an ellipse or an hyperbola with axes varying with x.

Conic markings are commonly observed in PMMA and arise from this mechanism (Fig. 6.6). The heterogeneity giving rise to the secondary fracture can sometimes be observed within the conic, though it is generally too small to be resolved by the light micro-scope. In fact the secondary fracture origins may be of molecular dimensions since they are found to increase in density as the mole-cular weight of the polymer decreases and may thus be associated with the structural discontinuities caused by molecular ends.[6] The mean spacing of parabola foci in some experiments on PMMA, for example, decreased progressively from about 100 μm for a molecular weight of $3\cdot2 \times 10^6$ to 1–5 μm for a molecular weight of 9×10^4. In Fig. 6.6 the whole fracture surface is occupied by secondary fractures, one secondary becoming the 'primary' for a further secondary and so on. The actual conic figures are traced out by small steps indicating that the various secondary figures occupy slightly different planes, though there are also faint striae radiating from the points of initiation to the conic boundaries which would betray the existence of secondary fracture even without the differences in plane. This effect can be seen in the brittle fracture of a glassy polymer containing carbon black filler, an electron micrograph of which is shown in Fig. 6.7. Although there is no consistent difference in level between the surfaces of different secondary fractures, their separate existence is clear from the radiating striae, usually originating at filler particles. In this case the boundaries of the regions are roughly circular suggesting that the primary fracture was moving very rapidly compared with the secondaries $(v \gg u)$ and this is consistent with the small size of the secondary fracture regions. Fig. 6.7 provides an interesting example of the dangers of misinterpretation of fracture markings since it could be easily mistaken for a picture of a spherulitically crystallised polymer, the secondary fracture regions forming the 'spherulites' and the striae the lamellae which compose it. The material was, however, undoubtedly an amorphous glass—natural rubber quenched from room temperature in liquid nitrogen!

(ii) *Surface roughness*

So far we have discussed the effect upon fracture surfaces of discreetly dispersed inhomogeneities, though the filler particles in the second example are much more closely spaced than the flaws which cause conic markings in PMMA. Viewed in a light microscope, in fact, the filler particles would not have been separately resolvable and the surface would have appeared simply to be slightly roughened. Variations in such surface roughness are characteristic of fracture surfaces viewed under the light microscope. Three broad degrees of roughness have been recognised, being named 'mirror', 'mist' and 'hackle' respectively. Mirrors are those regions of a fracture surface which reflect light specularly; mist refers to a matt surface in which, however, no separate features are resolvable and hackle is coarse roughness where fracture can be seen to have propagated on different levels over small areas of the surface. When the hackle is elongated in the direction of propagation of the fracture the term 'river markings' is often applied to it.

The three degrees of roughness are frequently seen in the same fracture surface and in all kinds of solids. A common observation is

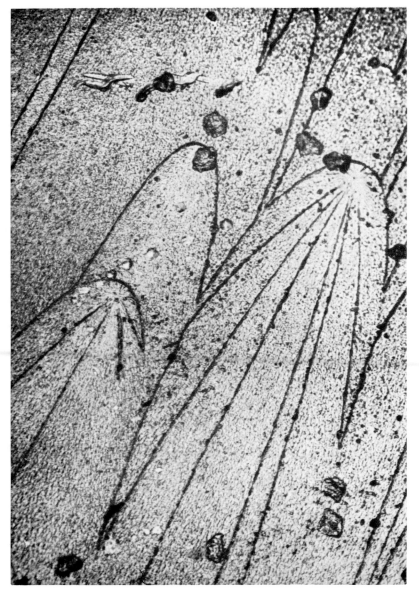

FIG. 6.6   Conic markings in a fast-fracture surface of PMMA. Magnification 180.

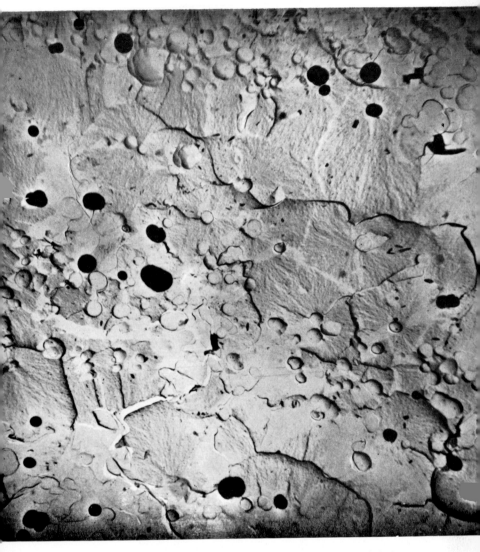

FIG. 6.7 Replica electron micrograph of a low-temperature brittle-fracture surface in a carbon filled rubber. Note secondary fracture regions centred on individual particles. Magnification 9000.

that a mirror region surrounds the origin of fracture but passes more or less suddenly into a zone of mist and finally into hackle at greater distances from the origin (Fig. 6.8). It is also found that slow fracture favours smooth surfaces and rapid fracture gives rise to rough ones. An explanation for this was given many years ago by Smekal [7] who studied these effects in glass. He postulated the existence of an even dispersion of flaws or stress raisers in the material and discussed the influence of these flaws on the propagating fracture. When the

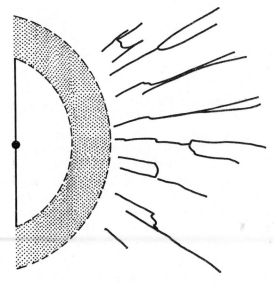

FIG. 6.8 Brittle-fracture surface showing (left to right)
fracture origin, mirror, mist and hackle regions.

fracture is dimensionally small, as we have seen in Chapter 4, the concentration of energy at the tip of the crack is also small or, to put it another way, the stress magnification at a *given* distance from the tip in any direction is directly related to the length of the crack. The likelihood of secondary fracture occurring at a given distance from the plane of the primary fracture thus increases as the crack propagates and if the primary front is diverted through these secondary fractures it will generate a surface roughness which also increases in severity with distance from the fracture origin. The same explanation applies to observed variations of roughness with velocity of fracture since slow fracture occurs under lower local stress than does fast fracture (cf. Chapter 3). A further striking illustration of this effect of the local stress level upon the surface roughness will be considered presently under the topic of 'Wallner phenomena'.

We have seen how differences of level, joined by sharp steps in the fracture surface, can be generated by diversion of the primary fracture through secondary fracture regions opened up in advance of the primary front. The further question must now be asked, what perpetuates a given difference of level once it has been established?

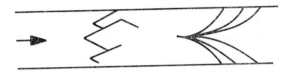

FIG. 6.9 Diamond and feather markings in a fracture surface.

This tendency is well established and gives rise to river markings and other curious geometrical features such as the 'diamond' markings and 'feathers' sketched in Fig. 6.9. There is no completely satisfactory answer to this but the explanation probably lies in the geometry of the stress field around the propagating fracture favouring a kind of stable forking of the fracture much as discussed in Chapter 5. Another way of expressing the same basic idea is to say that high speed fractures possess an excess of energy over and above that required for propagation, and multiplanar fracture and repeated forking are ways of absorbing this excess energy. We shall return to this idea of excess energy in the next section.

6.3 Markings Caused by Behaviour of the Fracture Front

The mirror surfaces mentioned earlier are typical of a 'well-behaved' fracture front propagating as a plane through the material and leaving a featureless surface in its wake. All deviations from this state of affairs have so far in this chapter been attributed to the existence of heterogeneity in the material and its interaction with the fracture process. It is possible, however, for deviations from planarity to occur in a perfectly homogeneous material and this may happen in two ways. Firstly in a perfectly elastic medium the normal progress of the fracture may be disturbed by interaction with travelling stress waves in the body and secondly where plasticity or visco-elasticity occur, the response of the material to the high local stresses at the fracture front may affect the progress of the latter and give rise to fracture markings.

(i) *Wallner lines*

Consider first the effect of travelling stress waves. These may be generated at the same point as the fracture originates by impact or by the sudden release of elastic energy. Travelling faster than the fracture, they may be reflected at the surfaces of the body and eventually meet the fracture front. According to their direction of approach they will momentarily both magnify and distort the stress distribution at the fracture front with a possible deviation of the front from its original direction. Sometimes this deviation is periodic because a train of regularly spaced stress impulses interact with the travelling fracture and the surface becomes undulating. This phenomenon was first described by Wallner [8] and now bears his name. It has been extensively studied in glass and its cause established by experiments in which a specimen was irradiated by ultrasonic waves generated *externally* throughout the duration of fracture.[9,10] An evenly rippled surface resulted, the periodicity and orientation of the ripples immediately providing a measure of the fracture velocity in terms of the known frequency of irradiation. True Wallner phenomena, of course, rely upon self-generated stress waves to produce this periodicity in the fracture surface.

Wallner lines have been observed in polymers though in the cases so far reported they do not take the form of smooth undulations as in glass but rather of periodic variations in surface roughness.[11] This is no doubt because polymeric solids are less homogeneous than glass and the momentarily increased local stress caused by the passage of a stress pulse results in more widespread secondary fracture rather than a deviation of the fracture plane. Wallner effects in carbon-filled rubber cooled to the glassy state and fractured in a brittle manner are shown in Fig. 6.10(a). Various systems of wave-like markings are visible in the surface of the specimen and can be shown by interference microscopy to be formed from alternate bands of 'mirror' and 'mist' in the fracture surface. Where two bands of mist intersect, incipient hackle is often seen as would be expected by the simultaneous arrival of two stress pulses at the fracture front.

Fig. 6.10(b) reveals the origin of the different systems of Wallner Lines. One system, concentric with the fracture front, can be attributed to interaction of the front with stress pulses generated immediately behind the front itself. Other systems, marked 2, 3 and 4 in Fig. 6.10(b) can be shown to correspond to the arrival at the fracture front of reflections of the same stress pulses from the specimen surfaces. System 2 relates to the first reflection from the upper surface, system 3 to the first from the lower surface and system 4 to the second reflection from the upper surface. Intersecting Wallner line systems have also been observed in fast fracture surfaces in PMMA and this is illustrated in Fig. 6.11.

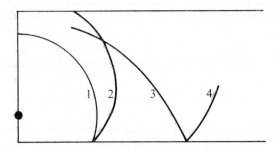

FIG.   6.10(b) Origin of the Wallner markings in Fig. 6.10(a)
(after Andrews[11]).

These observations provide some interesting information about Wallner phenomena. Firstly the very fact that various systems overlap prove conclusively that the periodic surface markings cannot be due to stick-slip behaviour of the fracture front since this could only generate a single system of such markings. Thus even the concentric system is seen to be due to travelling stress waves and the fracture can be thought to 'photograph' an already existing state of stress in the body as it travels through it. Secondly the identification of the various systems of lines pinpoints the origin of the stress pulses as the relaxing region immediately behind the fracture front itself. This region must therefore be in oscillation, a conclusion which seems eminently reasonable for a crack possessing an excess of energy beyond that required for its propagation.

Other periodic changes of surface roughness may also be attributable to the Wallner effect, such as those reported in PMMA and polystyrene [12] but not explained by the authors and the same may

FIG. 6.10(a) Wallner lines produced by low-temperature brittle fracture in a carbon filled rubber. Magnification 110 (after Andrews[11]).

FIG. 6.11   Intersecting Wallner lines in a fast-fracture surface of PMMA. Magnification 180.

be true of the *sudden* transition from a mirror region surrounding the fracture origin to a rougher surface sometimes observed and particularly evident in the case of glassy-state rubber discussed above. Smekal's explanation would only account for a gradual change whereas it is very often abrupt and associated with the onset of periodic effects. It seems likely that the limit of the mirror zone marks the size at which the fracture first finds itself with an excess of energy part of which then begins to be radiated as stress waves with the consequent production of Wallner lines.

(ii) *Stick-slip behaviour*

A second class of fracture markings found in homogeneous materials are those arising from 'stick-slip' behaviour of the fracture. As a crack grows in size it tends to accelerate because more and more energy is available for its propagation. There is, as we have seen, an upper limit to the velocity of fracture and one might expect acceleration to continue up to this point and then to cease, allowing the fracture to propagate at its maximum permissible speed. In many cases however the acceleration of the fracture gives rise to instability, the most common example of this being crack forking in which the fracture divides into two separate branches and is either halted or slowed down before one of the branches continues to propagate. This process may be repeated again and again giving rise to a quasi-periodic effect. This could be confused with the Wallner phenomenon especially as the surfaces generated during rapid propagation tend to be smooth whilst those associated with slow propagation (the 'stick' regions) are often rough. In this case, however, the periodicity is much less regular and the surface roughness is the *cause* of reduced crack velocity rather than the *result* of a momentary increase in local stress. Fig. 6.12 illustrates the 'stick-slip' propagation of fracture in a rubber, the length of the crack being plotted against time so that the tangent to the plot at any point gives the instantaneous velocity.[13] The maximum velocity achieved was comparable with theoretical expectations but frequently the fracture was brought almost to a standstill.

Periodic markings concentric with the fracture origin are commonly found in the tensile fracture of glassy polymers and have generally been attributed to stick-slip behaviour, though in the light of the foregoing discussion of Wallner phenomena this may still be considered an open question. A typical tensile fracture in PMMA exhibits a circular mirror surrounding the fracture origin which gives way to regions showing conic markings as discussed earlier but also containing circular 'ribs' the spacing of which increases with distance from the origin. The size of the mirror zone is a function of a number of variables. Zandeman [14] found that very large mirror regions were obtained at low rates of loading and small ones at high rates. The mirror is also reduced in size by raising the temperature and the periodic rib markings also only appear at temperatures above 23°C. Finally, the spacing of the ribs decreases with decreasing molecular weight. These effects have not been satisfactorily explained but some

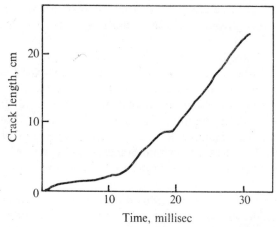

FIG. 6.12   Spreading of a fast crack in a sheet of SBR (after Mason[13]).

general considerations are outlined below. The effects in PMMA are, in particular, likely to depend upon the amount of plastic deformation possible in the vicinity of the propagating tip.

What causes the 'stick' phenomenon in polymeric materials? It was indicated earlier that crack forking was responsible in many cases and this can only occur if the stress distribution at the fracture tip changes in such a way as to encourage propagation along two loci instead of the usual single axial direction (Fig. 5.15). It has been shown that even a perfectly elastic solid may be subject to such changes in stress distribution when the fracture velocity reaches about 0·6 of the velocity of sound in the material and crack forking in, e.g., glass may be due to this purely elastic mechanism.[15] Once a fork has

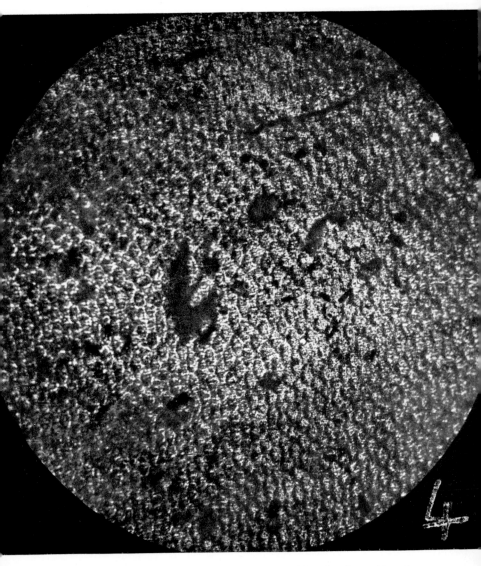

FIG. 6.14 Fatigue fracture surface in natural rubber showing quilt pattern generated when alternate segments of the fracture front deviate in opposite directions. Compare Fig. 5.24. Magnification 240.

developed the branches require twice the energy previously available if they are to continued unhindered (more than twice if they interact to give mutual relief of stress concentration), and often the crack is arrested altogether or else one branch continues at the expense of the other. Crack forking or deviation may arise at much lower velocities in polymers because of their visco-elastic nature and the reason for this has already been fully discussed in Chapter 5. The stress distribution at the tip of the fracture is modified in a similar way to that in the high speed elastic fracture so that propagation along two loci is encouraged. Sometimes forking occurs leaving a series of typical

FIG. 6.13   Undercutting of a fracture surface caused by crack forking.

undercut mounds on the fracture surface (Fig. 6.13). The way in which the maximum stress loci govern the appearance of fatigue fracture surfaces has been discussed already in Chapter 5 (see Figs. 5.24 and 5.25). Occasionally alternate segments of the crack front turn from the axis in opposite directions and the quilt-like markings illustrated in Fig. 6.14 are generated.

(iii) *Local plastic deformation*

Just as the elastic and visco-elastic responses of the material to the high stress at the fracture tip give rise to fracture markings in homogeneous solids, so the plastic response of a material also manifests itself. The effect of plastic flow upon the stress distribution at a crack is to lower the maximum stresses and distribute them uniformly over a wider region (Fig. 6.15). It follows that a fracture propagates on a much broader front and leaves behind it a swathe of plastically deformed material which thus constitutes a layer on each fracture surface. This is the most likely explanation of the striking colours seen in the fracture surfaces of some plastics, notably PMMA.[16] The colours are caused by interference between light reflected from the surface and light reflected from the interface between the plastically deformed layer and the undeformed substrate (Fig. 6.16). It has been argued that the difference in refractive index between the oriented

molecules of the surface layer and the unoriented ones of the
substrate in PMMA is too small to explain the effect since insufficient
light would be reflected at the interface, and it is suggested instead
that sub-surface cracks may be responsible. This does not allow,

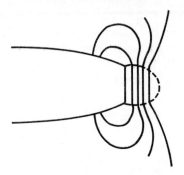

FIG. 6.15 Iso-stress lines around a
crack tip where plastic flow has occurred
(schematic).

however, for the many voids which must be present in the oriented
material since it occupies a greater apparent volume after plastic
deformation than before, and these voids could easily introduce the
necessary difference of refractive index. The plastically deformed

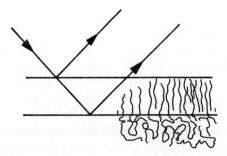

FIG. 6.16 Interference of light at a plastically
deformed (oriented) surface layer.

layer varies in thickness but is of the order of 0·3 μm on each
surface as estimated from the interference colours.

In PMMA at room temperature the degree of plasticity is, of
course, small and the void texture generated in the fracture surface

is sub-microscopic. In more highly plastic materials where the voids may be much larger it is possible to produce the 'fibrous' type of fracture typical of ductile failure in metals. Haward and Mann [17] observed such evidence of ductility around the rubbery inclusions of an acrylonitrile-butadiene-styrene copolymer.

6.4 THE STUDY OF STRESS-CORROSION PHENOMENA BY MICROSCOPY

The direct microscopy and electron microscopy of surfaces has provided much vital information about the nature and mechanism of stress-corrosion cracking in polymers. The quantitative aspects of this fracture mode have already been discussed at length in Chapter 5 and reference has already been made to the broad results of microscopical studies. Here we shall consider in more detail the qualitative features revealed by microscopy.

In these studies it is not always the actual fracture surface which is examined but rather the exposed surface in which corrosion cracks occur. It is often possible to trace the development of these cracks from the point of initiation to their final macroscopic forms and so to obtain evidence concerning the mechanisms by which they come into being and propagate themselves.

(i) *Stress-corrosion cracks in glassy polymers*

In addition to the observations on crack population and size previously referred to in Chapter 3, some account has been given of the micromorphology of a single craze crack. Bessonov and Kuvshinskii[18] used a two beam light interference technique to study the internal shape of craze cracks in plasticised PMMA and obtained the profiles shown in Fig. 6.17. Here y is the width of the crack in the direction of the applied stress and x is the depth of penetration of the crack into the attacked surface. The profile of penetrating craze cracks in a plane *perpendicular* to the applied stress appears to be irregular, unlike that of ozone cracks in rubbers which are almost perfectly semi-circular (Fig. 6.18, see later). The imperfect profile in glassy polymers may be a consequence of the 'craze matter' (see Chapter 3.4) which fills such cracks in glassy plastics diminishing the severity of the mechanical discontinuity at the crack boundaries and encouraging a rather irregularly shaped fracture front.

Micrographs of the craze matter itself [19] suggest that it possesses a drawn, fibrous texture with a high void content. This is in harmony with its known composition and with its probable mode of formation

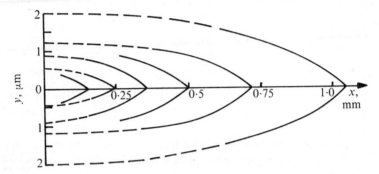

FIG. 6.17   Craze-crack profiles in PMMA (after Bessonov and Kuvshinskii[18]).

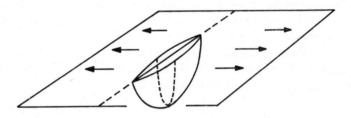

FIG. 6.18   Profile of an ozone crack in a rubber surface. Arrows show direction of stress.

by the orientation of chain molecules under stress, facilitated by the penetration of solvent which acts as a plasticiser for the stressed material.

(ii) Ozone cracking in elastomers

Replica electron microscopy has been used to follow the initiation and growth of submicroscopic ozone cracks in unsaturated hydrocarbon elastomers and has proved of great value in elucidating the role of various protective measures such as the incorporation of chemical antiozonants or of a second ozone-inert phase.[20,21,22] Below the critical strain for cracking, exposure of the rubber surface to ozone results in the formation of a degraded layer which protects the underlying rubber from further rapid atttack. Although in

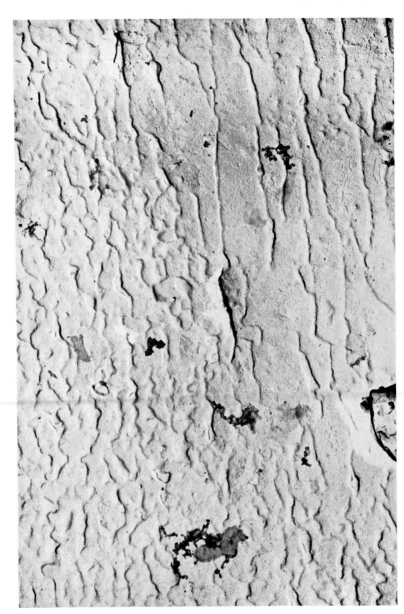

FIG. 6.19 Replica electron micrograph of incipient ozone cracking in a rubber surface showing oriented etch pits and true cracks. Magnification 20 000 (after Andrews and Braden[20]).

Fig. 6.21 Replica showing two parallel ozone cracks in the surface of a NR/EPR blend. Note EPR particles unsevered by the cracks. Magnification 10 000 (after Andrews[2]).

principle this surface degradation should be quite uniform it is often thickly populated with etch pits which indicate a more rapid penetration of ozone at some points than at others. These etch pits may be attributed to the presence of internal biaxial surface strains probably arising from uneven vulcanisation during moulding of the specimen. As uniaxial strain is superimposed on these residual strains the etch pits become oriented and assume the form of cracks. In regions of the surface where no etch pits are observed, much finer cracks are suddenly found to occur as the strain exceeds some critical value. Fig. 6.19 shows both of these kinds of region (i.e., oriented etch pits and fine cracks) in the same surface.

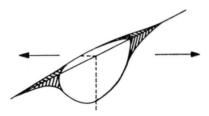

FIG. 6.20   Sectional view of an ozone crack in a rubber surface showing, shaded, the leader cracks. Arrows show direction of stress.

The time for the accumulation of a given amount of surface damage decreases as the strain increases. This does not conflict with the observations of Braden and Gent [22] that a single macroscopic ozone crack propagates at a rate independent of stress (once the latter exceeds the critical value) since here we are concerned with the penetration of *surface* cracks which will be governed by the ability of the crack to spread along the surface. With such cracks, unlike those used by Braden and Gent (see Fig. 5.26), attack can occur in the surface in *advance* of the crack. This gives rise to what may be described as a 'leader' crack which strictly speaking is not part of the main crack at all but which nevertheless facilitates the spread of the main crack. This mechanism is illustrated in Fig. 6.20. The higher the stress level, the farther in advance of the main crack can the leader crack run with a resultant increase in the overall rate of a propagation.

As Fig. 6.19 indicates, the cracks formed initially are very numerous, being spaced only about 1 μm or less apart. By contrast, macroscopic cracks are typically several mm apart and it follows that

14

only very few of the original cracks survive to attain macroscopic dimensions. This process of crack healing is observed in electron micrographs, the healing being caused of course by the relief of surface stresses occasioned by the presence of numerous cracks. A statistically determined proportion of the cracks survive but the remainder first heal up and are subsequently obliterated by the gradual progression of overall degradation.

The role of chemical antiozonants in the protection of surfaces against ozone attack does not particularly concern us here since their effect is simply to replace the degraded layer formed in their absence, by a coherent ozone-resistant layer, increasing either the time or the energy required to initiate cracking. An alternative form of ozone-protection, however, is of considerable interest because it involves the physical blockage of propagating cracks. It has been found that blends of elastomers containing both an ozone-reactive and an ozone-inert phase displayed superior ozone-resistance to the parent reactive polymer and electron microscopy has again helped to explain the mechanisms by which this resistance is imparted.

The critical stored energy required in such a blend for the formation of macroscopic ozone cracks increases with the proportion of resis-tant phase. A study [2] of a range of natural rubber ethylene-propylene rubber blends indicated that microscopic cracks formed in all the blends but that the cracks were, here and there, forced to bridge particles of the inert phase without severing them (Fig. 6.21). This bridging occurs when the stress concentration at the crack tip is of sufficient intensity to project a high stress *beyond* any inert particle it may encounter, thus initiating a new crack at the far side of the particle concerned. Since the stress concentration at a crack is related to its length and the overall stress field the likelihood of such a jump (and thus of the survival of the crack) decreases with the proportion of inert material and increases with the overall stored energy in the specimen. An increase in the inert phase must thus be offset by an increase in the stored energy to cause macroscopic cracking. The crack jump theory is supported by quantitative agree-ment with experiment.

6.5 SUMMARY

The use of microscopy and associated techniques provides a great deal of information about fracture phenomena and in particular about fracture mechanisms and must always be an important tool in the study of this subject. Although the information gained is essentially qualitative it has sometimes been possible to provide quantitative tests of theory in a well-designed experiment. The fact that fracture, though of macroscopic practical importance, is always in a vital sense a microscopic phenomenon underlines the necessity of the approach discussed in this chapter. The use of microscopy can be expected to increase especially in the topical realm of the relationship between fracture properties and microstructure considered briefly in Chapter 3.

References

1. ANDREWS, E. H., and WALSH, A. *Proc. Phys. Soc.*, **72**, 42 (1958).
2. ANDREWS, E. H. *J. appl. Polym. Sci.*, **10**, 47 (1966).
3. ANDREWS, E. H., and TURNER, D. T. *J. appl. Polym. Sci.*, **3**, 366 (1960).
4. GEIL, P. H. *Polymer Single Crystals*, p. 232, John Wiley and Sons, Inc. (1963).
5. LEEUWERIK, J., and SCHWARZL, F. *Plastica*, **8**, 474 (1955).
6. NEWMAN, S. B., and WOLOCK, I. *J. Res. Natl Bur. Std.*, **58**, 339 (1957). *J. appl. Phys.*, **29**, 49 (1958).
7. SMEKAL, A. *Ergeb. Exakt. Naturw.*, **15**, 106 (1936).
8. WALLNER, H. *Z. Physik*, **114**, 368 (1939).
9. KERKHOF, F. *Naturwissenschaften*, **40**, 478 (1953).
10. SCHARDIN, H. *Fracture* (ed. B. L. Averbach), p. 298, John Wiley and Sons, Inc. (1959).
11. ANDREWS, E. H. *J. appl. Phys.*, **30**, 740 (1959).
12. WOLOCK, I., *et al. Fracture* (ed. B. L. Averbach), p. 250, John Wiley and Sons, Inc. (1959).
13. MASON, P. *J. appl. Phys.*, **29**, 1146 (1958).
14. ZANDEMAN, F. *Étude de la Déformation et de la Rupture des Matières Plastiques*, Publications Scientifiques et Techniques du Ministère de l'Air, Paris (1954).
15. YOFFE, E. H. *Phil. Mag.*, **42**, 739 (1951).
16. BERRY, J. P. *Nature*, **185**, 91 (1960).
17. HAWARD, R. N., and MANN, J. *Proc. R. Soc.*, A, **282**, 120 (1964).

18. BESSONOV, M. I., and KUVSHINSKIĬ, E. V. *Soviet Phys.-Solid State*, **3**, 950 (1961).
19. SPURR, O. K., and NIEGISCH, W. D. *J. appl. Polym. Sci.*, **6**, 585 (1962).
20. ANDREWS, E. H., and BRADEN, M. *J. Polym. Sci.*, **55**, 787 (1961).
21. ANDREWS, E. H., and BRADEN, M. *J. appl. Polym. Sci.*, **7**, 1003 (1963).
22. BRADEN, M., and GENT, A. N. *J. appl. Polym. Sci.*, **3**, 90 (1960).

Author Index

Subject Index